Practical Meat Cutting and Merchandising

VOLUME 2
PORK, LAMB, VEAL

NEW AVI soft cover textbook series

STORY OF FOOD   *Garard*
FOOD AND THE CONSUMER   *Kramer*
FOOD FOR THOUGHT   *Labuza*
PRACTICAL BAKING WORKBOOK[1]   *Sultan*

Other AVI textbooks of interest to the young student

TECHNOLOGY OF FOOD PRESERVATION, 3rd EDITION   *Desrosier*
MENU PLANNING   *Eckstein*
PRACTICAL MEAT CUTTING AND MERCHANDISING, VOL. 1 BEEF   *Fabbricante and Sultan*
FOOD SANITATION   *Guthrie*
WORK ANALYSIS AND DESIGN IN FOOD SERVICE   *Kazarian*
FOOD SERVICE FACILITIES PLANNING   *Kazarian*
FOOD PRODUCTS FORMULARY, VOL. 1 MEATS, POULTRY, FISH, AND SHELLFISH   *Komarik, Tressler, and Long*
PROCESSED MEATS   *Kramlich, Pearson, and Tauber*
THE MEAT HANDBOOK, 3rd EDITION   *Levie*
LIVESTOCK AND MEAT MARKETING   *McCoy*
POULTRY PRODUCTS TECHNOLOGY   *Mountney*
COMMERCIAL CHICKEN PRODUCTION MANUAL   *North*
FOOD SCIENCE, 2nd EDITION   *Potter*
FOOD PACKAGING   *Sacharow and Griffin*
FOOD SERVICE SCIENCE   *Smith and Minor*
PRACTICAL BAKING, 2nd EDITION   *Sultan*
CONVENIENCE AND FAST FOOD HANDBOOK   *Thorner*
FOOD BEVERAGE SERVICE HANDBOOK   *Thorner and Herzberg*
BEVERAGES: CARBONATED AND NONCARBONATED   *Woodroof and Phillips*
SCHOOL FOODSERVICE   *Van Egmond*

---

[1]This soft cover book of lesson units and questionnaires is a companion workbook for the hard cover textbook *Practical Baking*, 2nd EDITION by Sultan.

Practical Meat Cutting and Merchandising—Volume 2 Pork, Lamb, Veal

by THOMAS FABBRICANTE

Chairman, Meat Cutting and Merchandising Department, Food & Maritime High School, New York, N.Y.
Training and Curriculum Consultant

and WILLIAM J. SULTAN

Assistant Principal and Supervisor of Training, Food Trades, Food & Maritime High School, New York, N.Y.
Educational Consultant, Lecturer, and Demonstrator, Baking and Allied Foods

WESTPORT, CONNECTICUT
THE AVI PUBLISHING COMPANY, INC.
1975

Printed in the United States of America

Preface

The objectives of this text, *Practical Meat Cutting and Merchandising—Pork, Lamb, Veal*, are similar to those defined in the preface of the text *Practical Meat Cutting and Merchandising—Beef*. In essence, this preface will repeat the same purposeful goals that will hopefully be achieved by all who will use this text as a teaching-learning vehicle, as well as a practical reference resource. More specifically, this text is directed to all who are engaged in the purchase, processing, merchandising, distribution, and preparation of a variety of meats for human consumption and to enable them to perform more efficiently and effectively within the sphere of their respective areas of work.

The contents of this manual are directly concerned with the processing and merchandising of pork, lamb, and veal. As such, it meets the needs of the instructor of meat cutting and merchandising, the wholesale and retail meat cutters and purveyors of meat, the apprentice meat cutter, the chef and cook, and those in managerial and supervisory positions in the food and hospitality industry whose responsibilities include the purchase of a variety of meats and the planning of menus in which these meats are used. This text may also serve as a valuable source of information and guidance to the home economist and the consumer. A better understanding and knowledge of pork, lamb, and veal, in conjunction with domestic cooking skill, can be a decided asset toward the improvement of meal planning, food service, and budget control.

For the instructor of meat cutting and merchandising, the format of the text will simply and directly explain, illustrate, and stress the specifics necessary for skill development. Equal emphasis will be placed upon related trade information and merchandising factors directly associated with the skill. Special emphasis will be particularly directed toward the development of safe work habits through the practice and understanding of safe work procedures. In addition, the important regulations and requirements of Federal and State agencies that govern and control the processing and merchandising of meats will be included.

The manual is divided into three major sections, each concerned with the processing and merchandising of pork, of lamb, and of veal. Each of the sections are subdivided into units. Each of the units follows a chronological sequence of steps and is supplemented with illustrations showing the exact procedures for each of the steps or operations of the job. This format will enable the instructor, the student, the apprentice, and those with limited or specialized experience with other meats to select specific units within each of the major meat areas for review, self-instruction, or for the training of personnel in selective areas. Emphasis is placed upon the merchandising aspects related to these units. One aspect of merchandising is stressed through suggested methods of cooking. Suggested dishes also accompany these cooking suggestions since many attractive and inviting meat menu items are derived from pork, lamb, and veal. These should be of interest to the consumer as well as educating the consumer to get maximum value and results from the prepared meat dish.

Acknowledgement

The two volumes of *Practical Meat Cutting and Merchandising* covering beef, pork, lamb, and veal contain a total of 470 illustrations. Acknowledgement for executing these drawings is hereby given to

Daniel Long, B.S., B.F.A., M.A.
Art Coordinator,
Joel Barlow High School,
Regional District No. 9,
Redding, Connecticut

and

Edward A. Hine,
Technical Illustrator,
17 Ash Street,
Fairfield, Connecticut

Contents

Introduction: Trade Terms Related to Pork, Lamb, and Veal

AITCH BONE   The split pelvic bone, exposing the surface of the bone on the inside portion of the rounds.   The posterior end of the pelvic bone.

ANTEMORTEM   Before death.

ANTERIOR   Refers to the head or front portion of the carcass.

AORTA   Largest artery of the carcass. Generally found on the rib and loin section of the carcass close to the chine bone.

BACK BACON   *See* Canadian-Style Bacon.

BACON SQUARE   Cured and smoked pork jowl. Referred to as jowl bacon.

BARROW   Young castrated male member of the swine family approximately 6 months of age.

BEAN PORK   A cured, salted jowl or fat back, usually squared.

BELLY   That portion of the pork side remaining after the removal of the untrimmed shoulder and ham, the pork loin, and the spareribs removed from the belly.

BLACK GUT   Large convoluted intestine of a hog. Generally merchandised as chitterlings.

BLADE MEAT   Refers to lean meat which is derived from the Boston butt located in the blade bone section of the butt.

BOAR   Mature old male of the swine family, generally used for breeding purposes.   Can be of any age.

BOB VEAL   Immature veal carcass usually under 10 days of age.

BONE DUST   Fine particles of bone on the cut surface of retail items cut on the band saw.

BONE SOUR   A putrefaction that may sometimes develop in the bones of slaughtered animals.

BOSTON BUTT   Dorsal side of the pork shoulder containing the blade bone.

BREAK JOINT   A characteristic trait to distinguish between lamb and mutton.   Not a true joint.   This is the separation of cartilage from bone on the front feet of lamb carcasses.

BRINE   Water containing dissolved salt, with or without chemicals. Used for curing meats.

BUCK   An uncastrated old member of the mutton class. Generally used for reproduction.

BUTTONS   The white tips of undeveloped bone generally found on the end of feather bones in the backbone section of the carcass. It is an indication of youth in the carcass.

CALVES   Young member of the bovine species (cattle family) approximately 3 to 8 months of age.

CANADIAN-STYLE BACON   Boneless pork loin, minus the tenderloin, which is cured and smoked.   Also known as back bacon.

CARBON DIOXIDE (CO_2)   Colorless, odorless gas used for chemical stunning of hogs. Under pressure it will become Dry Ice.

CHINE BONE   The split vertebral column, the ventral edge of the backbone.   Soft red chine bones indicate youth; white, hard flinty chine bones indicate aged.

CHITTERLINGS   *See* Black Gut.

CHUCK (LAMB)   That portion of the lamb carcass remaining after the removal of the long hindsaddle.

CHUCK WITH WINGS ON (LAMB)   That portion of the lamb carcass remaining after the removal of the trimmed back and a pair of lamb legs.

CLEAR PLATE   A layer of fat with rind attached which is removed from the Boston butt.

CONNECTIVE TISSUE   A tissue which supports and binds other tissues in the lean of a carcass.

CORNING   *See* Brine.

COUNTRY-STYLE SPARERIBS   Approximately 3 ribs removed from the pork loin (shoulder side) with the meat attached to the bone. Generally merchandised as country-style bar-b-que ribs.

CROWN ROAST   Roast prepared from the rib section of a pork loin or a lamb rack. Resembles the shape of a king's crown.

CUSHION OF HAM   Side of fresh ham which is more rounded and fleshy.   It is generally on the side where the inside round muscle is located.

DIAPHRAGM   The skirt section of the carcass. The large thin sheet of muscle which separates the chest and abdominal cavity.

DRY CURED   Meat cured by rubbing salt directly into the surface of the meat.

EVISCERATE   Removal of the internal organs.

EWE   A class of mutton.   Female member of the sheep family. Generally used for reproduction purposes.

FACING HAMS   Removal of surplus fat from the inside surface of the fresh ham.

FALSE LEAN   Thin layer of meat on the outside surface of the pork loin located on the rib side (overlaying meat).

FEATHER BONES   The dorsal portion of the split backbone protruding from the spinal column.   White cartilage on ends indicate youth.

FELL   Reference term generally used with lamb retail cuts.   A thin layer of membrane located between the skin and layer of fat beneath the skin.

FINGER BONES   Bones protruding from the backbone between the tenderloin muscle and the loin eye muscle.

FINGER MEAT   Small pieces of meat found between the rib bones.   These trimmings are generally obtained during the boning (scalping) of any rib section of the carcass.

FIVE-WAY BREAKDOWN (LAMB)   Method of cutting a lamb carcass into five subprimal cuts.

FORESADDLE   That portion of a carcass remaining after the removal of the hindsaddle. Refers to the front portion of the carcass.

FOUR-WAY BREAKDOWN (LAMB)   Method of cutting a lamb carcass into four subprimal cuts.

GIBLETS (PORK)   Refers to the skirt, hanging tender, aorta, and leaf fat covering the tenderloin on a pork loin (regular).

GILT   Young female member of the swine family, generally 6 months of age and weighs from 150 to 250 lb.

HAM (BUTT HALF)   That portion of the fresh ham which contains the aitch bone, tail bone, and the ball portion of the leg bone.

HAM (FRESH)   That portion of the untrimmed ham remaining after the removal of the hind foot, tail, and the flank.

HAM (SHANK HALF)   That half of the fresh ham which contains the leg, shank, and kneecap bones.   The shank portion is usually covered with rind (skin).

HINDSADDLE   That portion of the carcass remaining after the removal of the foresaddle. Refers to the rear portion of the carcass.

HOT-HOUSE LAMBS   Generally referred to as baby lambs usually appearing on the market during the Easter holiday season.   They are generally raised in confined quarters.

LAMB   Young member of the sheep family.

LAMB COMBINATION   Generally refers to the retail cut items of stews, chops, and roasts, all packaged in one boat.

LAMB LEGS (PAIR)   That portion of the lamb carcass remaining after the removal of the long foresaddle.

LAMB SHOULDER   One half of a lamb chuck which is split down the center of the backbone.

LAMB STEAKS   Slices of lamb taken from the center portion of the lamb leg.

LOIN BACK RIBS   Taken from the rib side of the pork loin with meat between the rib bones. These ribs are generally removed during the boning process (scalping).

LONG FORESADDLE   That portion of a the lamb carcass remaining after the removal of a pair of lamb legs.

LONG HINDSADDLE   That portion of the lamb carcass remaining after the removal of the lamb chuck.

MAW (HOG)   Pork stomach.

MUTTON   Class of sheep. Mature member of the sheep family.

NATURE VEAL   The best quality of veal. Young member of the bovine species approximately 16 weeks of age.   Usually raised in confined quarters with a scientific controlled diet.

NECK BONES (PORK)   That portion of bones removed in one piece from the untrimmed shoulder, containing the neck bones, rib bones, feather bones, and breast bone all in one piece.

OSSO BUCCO   Italian-style dish prepared from veal hindshanks with the bone in.

OVERLAYING MEAT   See False Lean.

OVINE SPECIES   Sheep family.

OYSTER MEAT   Small round portion of intermingling lean and fat located in the cavity of the aitch bone.

PATTY   Various sized disc-shaped ground portion of meat, with or without other ingredients.

PICNIC   Ventral side of pork shoulder containing the arm bone, shank bone, and socket portion of the balde bone.

PORK CHOPS (SHOULDER OR BLADE)   Approximately 4 to 5 chops cut from the shoulder end of the pork loin containing the blade bone or blade bone cartilage.

PORK CHOPS (HIP OR SIRLOIN)   Approximately 4 to 5 chops cut from the loin end of the pork loin containing the hip portion of the pelvic bone.

PORK CHOPS (CENTER CUT)   Chops cut from the center of the pork loin after the removal of the shoulder and hip ends.   Loin pork chops are cut from the loin side of the pork loin containing the tenderloin muscle.   Rib pork chops are cut from the rib side of the pork loin containing the rib bone.

PORK CUTLET Thin slice of lean pork (boneless).

PORK LOIN (REGULAR) That portion from a hog side remaining after the removal of the untrimmed ham, the untrimmed shoulder, the belly, and the back fat.

PORK LOIN (BLADELESS) Same as a regular pork loin plus the removal of the blade bone and cartilage and the overlying meat on the rib side (false lean).

PORK LOIN (CENTER-CUT) Same as a regular pork loin plus the removal of the hip end and the blade end.

PORTION CONTROL Cutting meat to a predetermined weight. Generally refers to individual portions.

POSTMORTEM After death.

PRESCAPULAR Refers to the portion of fat found in the front part of the shoulder which is located near the chuck tender muscle in the clod section of the carcass.

RIB CARTILAGES Costal cartilages which attach to the rib bones and the breast bone.

RIB EYE Major muscle which lies next to the backbone in the rib section of a carcass. Generally the eye muscle extends from the 6th rib to the 12th rib bone.

RIDGE OF BLADE BONE Protruding spine of the blade bone (scapula).

RIND Skin covering on hog carcass.

ROUGH CUT Generally refers to the belly region of the carcass including the flank, plate, brisket, and shank.

SALT Chemical name is NaCl, sodium chloride, used to season and preserve foods.

SARATOGA CHOPS Slices of the boneless rib eye muscle cut from the lamb shoulder (bottom chuck muscle). Generally used in the institutional trade.

SCALPING Process of boning, especially in the rib section of a carcass. Leaves a smooth inner surface on meat after boning.

SHACKLING Mechanical raising the animal by its hind leg on a bleeding rail before slaughter.

SHINGLED Type of packaging that includes the partial overlying of cut or sliced items in a container or tray.

SHRINKAGE The evaporation of water from a carcass or part of a carcass which results in a loss of weight during chilling or storage.

SINEW The tendonous ends which connect the skeletal portion of the carcass to the muscles.

SIRLOIN CHOPS (LAMB) Slices of lamb cut from the butt half of the lamb leg.

SKEWERS Wooden or metal pins used to hold cut cubes of meat. Generally refers to products such as shish kebab or brochettes.

SKIRT See Diaphragm.

SLIP JOINT Joint which connects the pelvic bone to the backbone.

SOW Matured old female of the swine family that has given birth to one or more litters of pigs.

SPARERIBS The entire intact rib section removed from the belly portion of the pork carcass.

SPINAL COLUMN A canal or tube of round form in the center of the backbone which contains the spinal cord.

SPOOLS Formation of bones in mature old carcasses of the sheep family found when the front feet are removed.

SPRING LAMB A class of lamb, young member of the sheep family.

STEWS (LAMB) See Chuck with Wings On (Lamb).

STIFLE JOINT Joint between the leg bone and the hind shank bone of a carcass.

STRAP (BACK) Large yellowish ligament near the backbone on the rib and neck portion of the carcass.

SWINE Refers to the porcine species.

TENDERLOIN Tender muscle located in the back region of the carcass in the loin area.

TENDON See Sinew.

THREE-WAY BREAKDOWN (LAMB) Method of cutting a lamb carcass into three subprimal cuts.

TRIMMED BACK (LAMB) That portion of a lamb carcass remaining after the removal of the chuck with wings on and a pair of lamb legs.

VEAL BRACELET That portion of the veal foresaddle remaining after the removal of the veal chuck regular.

VEAL CHUCKS & PLATES That portion of the veal foresaddle remaining after the removal of the hotel-style veal rack.

VEAL CHUCK (REGULAR) That portion of the veal foresaddle remaining after the removal of the veal bracelet.

VEAL CUTLET Thin boneless slice of veal.

VEAL FILETS Boneless rib eye muscle of the veal rack.

VEAL FORESADDLE That portion of the veal carcass remaining after the removal of the veal hindsaddle.

VEAL HINDSADDLE That portion of the veal carcass remaining after the removal of the veal foresaddle.

VEAL LEGS (PAIR)   That portion of the veal hindsaddle remaining after the removal of the veal loin.

VEALERS   Young members of the bovine species approximately 1 to 3 months of age.

VEAL RACK (HOTEL-STYLE)   That portion of the veal foresaddle remaining after the removal of the veal chucks and plates (double).

VEAL RACK (LONG)   That portion of the veal foresaddle remaining after the removal of the breast, the lifted veal shoulder, and the removal of the veal rack from the neck by cutting at the end of the 1st rib bone.   There are eleven rib bones in the long veal rack.

VEAL RACK (SHORT)   That portion of the veal foresaddle remaining after the removal of the breast, the lifted veal shoulder, and the removal of the veal rack from the neck by cutting between the 3rd and 4th rib bones.   There are eight rib bones in the short veal rack.

VEAL RUMP   That portion of the veal leg containing the pelvic bone and the tail bone.   The butt half of the veal leg.

VEAL SHOULDER CLOD   Boneless lifted veal shoulder.   Generally merchandised without the shank meat.

VEAL SQUARE-CUT CHUCK   That portion of the veal chuck regular remaining after the removal of the brisket and the foreshank.

VEAL STEAKS   Slices cut from the center portion of the veal leg.   Generally contain a small round portion of the leg bone.

VEAL T.B.S. (TOPS, BOTTOMS, SIRLOINS)   Boneless individual muscles processed from the veal leg.

VISCERA   The internal organs of an animal.

WEATHER   Matured male member of the mutton classes.   Generally castrated in the lamb stage.

WEDGE SHAPED   Irregular cut of steak or chop, thick on one side and thin on the other side.

YEARLING (LAMB)   Member of the sheep family, classed between the lamb and mutton stage.

YOKE (LAMB)   *See* Chuck with Wings On (Lamb).

Section I: PORK

UNIT 1: Pork Carcass Yield and Slaughter

Swine are descended from two strains of wild boars, the European and the Asiatic. The exact date of swine domestication is unknown, although records were found in eastern Asia as early as 2900 B.C., indicating that domestic swine were present. All modern breeds of hogs contain some characteristics of both European and Asiatic types. Hog breeders associations, swine producer groups, agricultural colleges, and other interested organizations contributed to the development of new breeds through cross breeding. The major emphasis is placed upon the production of meatier carcasses with more muscling and less fat. This results in a larger percentage of salable cuts with a minimum of trim. This type of hog is called a meat-type hog. The distinguishing characteristics of a meat-type hog are the meat muscle development and percentage of high yield of the four lean cuts: ham, loin, picnic, and Boston butt. A meat-type hog has a natural capacity and growing ability to reach a weight of approximately 200 lb within 6 months. It will retain all muscular development while being pushed for rapid gain. This type of hog is the most economical to raise because of the greater weight. They are more vigorous than the lard-type hog and are as prolific.

Grades and Yield

Hog carcass grades were first introduced in the United States in 1931 by the USDA.[1] They were revised in 1933. New standards were proposed in 1949 and they became effective in September 1952. They were revised again in July 1955, and again in April 1968. The principal basis for grades are (1) the quality-indicating characteristics or the lean (firmness, marbling, and color) and (2) the quantity (percentage) of the four lean cuts to a hog carcass. The term used in relation to these cuts is called "carcass cut-out." The Standards for grades of pork carcasses developed by USDA provide for segregation according to (1) Class, as determined by the apparent sex condition of the animal at the time of slaughter, and (2) Grade, which reflects the quality of pork and the relative proportion of lean cuts to fat cuts in the carcass. Carcasses will vary in their yields of the four major cuts because of their fat and muscle structure. Based on chilled carcass weight by grade, the percentage yield of the four lean cuts are:

Grade	Yield (%)
U.S. No. 1	53 and more
U.S. No. 2	50–52.9
U.S. No. 3	47–49.9
U.S. No. 4	Less than 47

Many carcasses have a normal distribution of fat and muscling. Therefore the average backfat thickness, carcass length, and weight are important factors in considering grades. To determine carcass length and backfat thickness study Fig. 1.1 on facing page showing where to measure carcass. These factors can be measured on a live hog with electronic instruments. One such instrument is called a lean meter. A complicated, but more accurate instrument, is called a sonaray. Although these instruments are not practical for everyday work, they are very important to the breeder in selecting stock which will produce litters representing the meat-type hog.

Actually, there are no grades of pork which the consumer can see on retail cuts of pork (as they do in beef and lamb). They must rely upon the quality the retailers purchase. Grades are very important to buyers at the packing house level, and are of increasing value to the meat industry in general.

The USDA lists five classes of pork carcasses: barrow, gilt, sow, stag, and boar. The most popular classes of pork carcass to reach the consumer in fresh pork cuts in most retail stores are the barrow and gilt classes.

Swine are generally classified by age. The young are called pigs and the more mature are called hogs. The flesh of these carcasses is called pork. Although the USDA does not place a baby or suckling pig into any class, it would be uniformly valuable to have it placed directly into the category of pigs because it is being retailed in prime meat stores.

Pigs are generally classified by age and sex. A baby or suckling pig is approximately up to 2

[1] USDA Grades for Pork Carcasses, Marketing Bull. *49*, U.S. Govt. Printing Office, Washington, D.C.

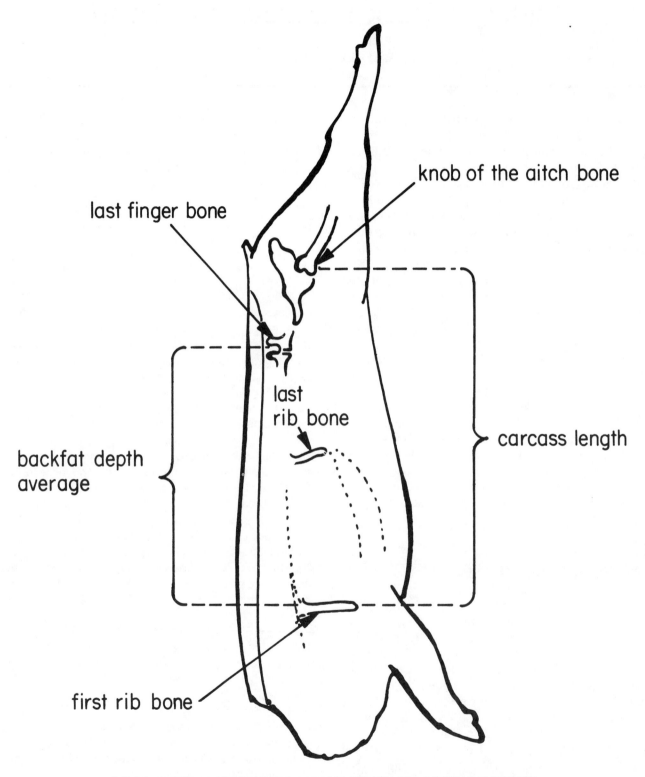

FIG. 1.1. WHERE TO MEASURE FOR CARCASS LENGTH AND BACKFAT THICKNESS

months of age and weighs between 10 and 50 lb, and can be of either sex. These carcasses are generally merchandised for festive or special occasions and sold fully dressed, in carcass form. A gilt is a female pig approximately 6-7 months of age and weighs from 150 to 250 lb. A barrow is a castrated male approximately 6-7 months of age and weighs from 150 to 300 lb. Hogs are also classified by sex. The sow is a matured, old female of the swine family that has given birth to one or more litters of pigs. A litter is composed of several young pigs born at the same time. A boar is a matured, old male of the swine family used for breeding purposes. A stag is a matured male of the swine family castrated after sexual maturity and may formerly have been used for breeding purposes.

The approximate range of dressing percentages for hogs of all classes and weights is from 68 to 75%. The average yield of a meat-type hog is about 70%. The following is quoted from USDA Marketing Bulletin *288:* Most beef, veal, calf, lamb, and mutton enters trade channels before any processing occurs; the meat is offered for sale to consumers in the same condition as when first dressed. Most pork, on the contrary, does not leave the packing plant in carcass form, nor in the form of quarters; most carcasses are divided into their primal cuts and into edible portions at the place of slaughter. Some of these cuts, approximately 15% of a carcass, are sold to consumers as fresh pork; the remaining 85% is cured by various methods, or rendered into lard, or is manufactured into meat products.

The small, round, purple, federal inspection stamp is a guarantee that the meat is derived from federally-inspected animals which were given antemortem and postmortem inspection by USDA meat inspectors to establish its fitness for food. All meat and meat products processed by packers who are engaged in interstate commerce are subject to federal inspection. Meat processed and sold within the state is subject to State and local inspection laws.

The first type of inspection (antemortem) takes place when the hogs are unloaded and placed in pens and is directed toward detection of contagious diseases. If it is found that the animal has a disease which renders it unfit for food, it is condemned. The first step of the second inspection (postmortem) takes place when the head is partly severed to expose the tonsils and the lymph glands. This inspection is to detect tuberculosis and other diseases affecting man. If there are any signs of disease, the carcass is tagged "U.S. Retained" and is sent to the "Retained Room" for further examination. If the disease is found to be

in more than one gland, even though it is not in the bloodstream, the carcass is likely to be condemned. No fresh meat from a condemned or retained carcass is ever sold. The next inspection is on the viscera. The intestines, heart, liver, and lungs are removed intact and their identity is maintained in the same manner as that of the carcass. At a later inspection, the various parts of the carcass for curing are further examined. All condemned carcasses remain in charge of the inspectors until they are tanked and rendered into commercial grease and tankage. As a result of these inspections the government assures the consumer that the meat is fit for human consumption.

Four Important Steps to Hog Slaughter

1. Immobilization

The chemical method employs carbon dioxide gas. The hogs ride in individual compartments down an incline into a chamber which holds a concentration of 65-75% carbon dioxide. The time of exposure to render the hog unconscious depends upon the size of the animal and the production rate. The advantage of this method is the elimination of excitement which causes fewer internal bruises, safer and better working conditions, more economical operation, and an improved product.

Studies were made at the University of Minnesota which indicated that internal bruises in hams can occur if the hind limb of a living hog is stretched at the time of shackling. It was also found that sticking in a prone position does not tear the cord in the ball and socket joint which will release blood to sour the flesh.

2. Scalding

Hogs are generally stuck after they have been placed in a shackle-hung position. After the hog has been stuck, it moves by conveyors to the scalding vat. A safe scalding temperature is between $130°$ and $142°$F. Overscalding causes the skin to contract around the base of the bristles, holding them tight; this is referred to as "setting the hair." An attendant then loosens the tendons so that the carcass can be supported on a gambrel stick.

3. Depilating

The carcass is then dehaired and the process of depilating consists of mechanically dipping each carcass into a hot solution of rosin and cottonseed oil for a period of 6-8 sec. The rosin-oil mixture consists of approximately 15% paraffin or cottonseed oil and 85% rosin. In some plants, the nostrils of the hogs are plugged with cotton, the mouth is closed by means of a clamp, and the bung is closed with a 6-in.-long dampened wooden plug to keep out the depilation compound. The compound forms a seal-like coating over the entire carcass. The heat turns the moisture present in the skin and on the outer surface into steam which penetrates to the roots of the hairs and loosens them. When the rosin coating has plasticized, it is stripped from the hog by pull-rolling it down the carcass.

4. Gutting

After the hair is removed from the carcass, it moves along a prescribed course where atten-

dants do specified tasks such as deheading, aitch bone splitting, breastbone splitting, bung dropping eviscerating, splitting or halving the carcass, removing leaf fat, exposing the kidneys for inspection, and facing the hams (removing the skin and fat from over the inside face or the cushion of the ham). Each carcass and its viscera are given a postmortem inspection. If found free from disease, the carcass is stamped "U.S. Inspected and Passed," and is then sent to the chill room. The quicker the carcass is properly chilled after slaughter the better will be the quality of the meat. It will keep longer, have a better bloom, and be more satisfactory to the consumer.

UNIT 2: Pork Loins

This unit deals with the pork loin and its relationship to processing and merchandising. Pork loins are one of the most popular fresh pork cuts, because they are so flexible in the variety of preparation and cooking. They are merchandised in various forms as chops and roasts. Many supervisors and managers may not be fully informed if they only conform to one particular method of merchandising pork loins. Flexibility will allow for variety in the types of cuts essential to meet the consumer demands within a community. This should also result in an increase in the tonnage of pork sales. These factors will be further developed as the unit progresses.

There are a variety of pork loins which can be purchased by the retailer. There are packing plants in the New York area, which do not slaughter hogs, but cut the dressed hog carcass into wholesale cuts. These wholesale cuts are generally placed in boxes and sold to wholesale houses, also known as provision houses, or sold directly to the retailer. Provision houses in the New York area also purchase wholesale cuts from packing plants in the corn belt region of the country. These specialized provision houses do not process any fresh meats. They only merchandise boxed meats, offal products, and sausage products which are generally packed in boxes or cartons.

Prices to the retail butcher will fluctuate from wholesaler to wholesaler depending upon the packer or the type of pork cut desired. Managers must use skill and knowledge in merchandising pork loins in a variety of methods to satisfy customer requests and also meet competitive prices. The degree to which these methods are employed will depend upon competition, customer, and store merchandising policies.

Pork loins are generally wrapped on the cutting floor of the packing house and placed in boxes. The type of paper used to wrap these loins is oiled manila or oiled white paper. This oiling process protects the pork loins from atmospheric effects and preserves their color.

Industry

Pork loins are generally classified by weight. Weight ranges are usually controlled in accordance with the methods used by the packer or the wholesaler in the processing of the loins. Pork loins will vary from one area or region to another. Some packers will use 2-, 3-, or 4-lb weight intervals. Some loins may weigh as little as 8 lb and some may weigh as much as 24 lb, the most common type being 14 lb and under. Other ranges are 14–17 lb, 17–20 lb, and 20 lb and up. Prices will vary, with the smaller weights being more expensive than the heavier weights. The most common weight of loin used for retail cuts is 14 lb and under. Some independent retail stores prefer to merchandise the lighter type of pork loins because the ends of the larger pork loins are difficult to merchandise.

This unit will treat this special type of merchandising to assist the meat cutter in developing skills and knowledge to efficiently merchandise pork loin ends. Heavier type pork loins are generally used by the packer in the production of Canadian-style bacon. Each box of pork loins is marked with the number of pork loins in the box, the weight range of the box, and the total weight of the pork loins in the box. The various types of pork loins purchased from the packer or wholesaler are identified as (1) regular pork loins, (2) regular pork loins extra trim, (3) bladeless pork loins, (4) fully bladeless pork loins, (5) fully bladeless pork loin extra trim, and (6) center cut pork loins. Some wholesale houses also merchandise pork loin ends. Because of the keen competition in chain stores and supermarkets, the most widely-used type of loin is the regular pork loin.

Let us examine the loin region on the pork carcass for its exact location (see Fig. 2.1). Loins from a live carcass will yield approximately $9\frac{1}{2}$%. In processing a pork loin from the carcass, the following procedures are employed on the cutting floor of the packing plant. The hog is split down the center of the backbone. The untrimmed shoulder is removed by cutting between the 2nd and 3rd rib bone perpendicular to the backbone. The untrimmed ham is removed by cutting $2\frac{1}{4}$ to $2\frac{3}{4}$ in. anterior (in front of) to the knob of the aitch bone at a slight angle. To remove the side from the loin, a cut is made extending from a point on the 3rd rib bone close to the chine bone, cutting through the rib bones and flank area, and ending on the loin side immediately adjacent to the tenderloin muscle. (Refer to Fig. 2.1.) The fat back is then removed from the untrimmed loin leaving $\frac{1}{4}$–$\frac{1}{2}$ in. of fat on the loin. The amount of fat remaining on the loin will often depend

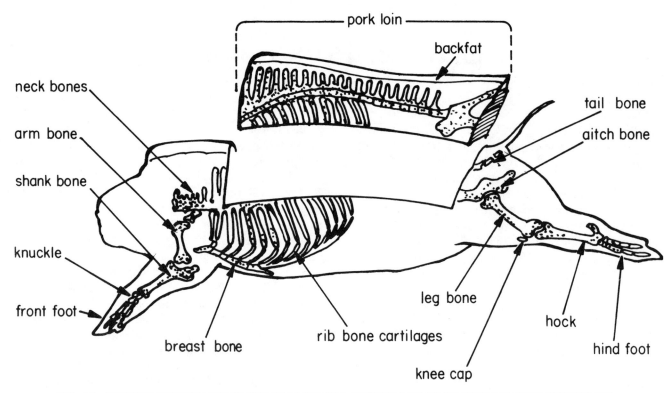

FIG. 2.1. POSITION OF THE LOIN IN THE CARCASS AND IDENTIFICATION OF CARCASS BONE STRUCTURE

upon the merchandising procedures employed in the packing plant. This type of operation is called "loin pulling" and is performed with a curved knife which has two handles. This technique generally results in an uneven amount of fat remaining on the regular pork loins.

Let us examine some important factors in the bone structure of the pork loin (see Fig. 2.2). Regular loins generally have between 13 and 15 rib

bones. This will depend on the method used in separating the loin from the shoulder at the packing plant. The loin is also composed of feather bones, finger bones, chine bones, a portion of the pelvic bone (known as the hip bone), the tail bone, and a small portion of the blade bone and cartilage found on the shoulder end of the pork loin (see Fig. 2.2). These bones represent approximately 22% of the loin. The fat represents 18%

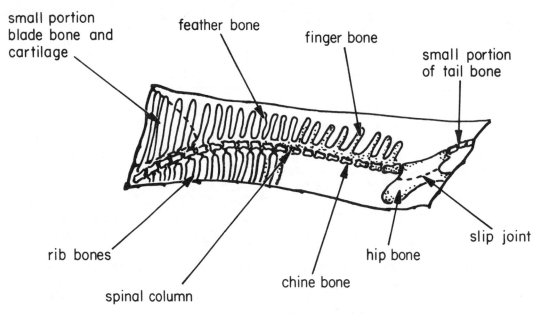

FIG. 2.2. BONE STRUCTURE OF THE REGULAR PORK LOIN

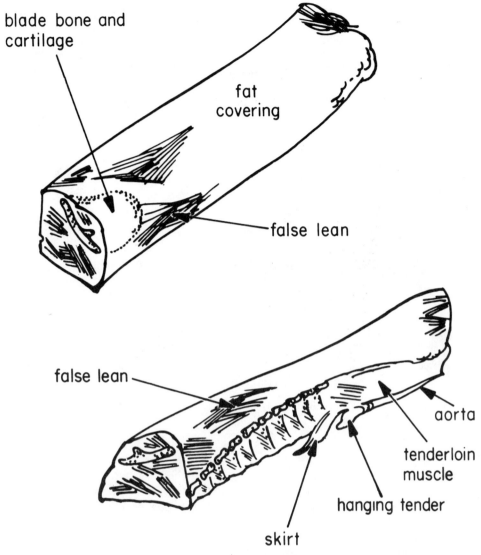

blade bone and cartilage

fat covering

false lean

false lean

aorta

tenderloin muscle

hanging tender

skirt

FIG. 2.3. OUTSIDE VIEW OF REGULAR PORK LOIN (ABOVE) AND INSIDE VIEW OF REGULAR PORK LOIN (BELOW)

and the lean is approximately 60%. To familiarize yourself with the regular loin, study Fig. 2.2. On the loin side of the loin there will be a small portion of the skirt, hanging tender, aorta, and fat covering the tenderloin muscle. The shoulder side of the loin is called the rib side which has a portion of lean meat. This meat is visible on the top portion of the loin. This meat is also known as the false lean (see Fig. 2.3).

Meat cutters generally refer to the chops from a regular loin as shoulder pork chops, rib and loin pork chops (called center cut pork chops), and hip pork chops (see Fig. 2.4). The true names (as defined by New York State Law) for pork chops derived from the regular pork loin are (1) shoulder or blade pork chops, (2) Rib pork chops, (3) loin pork chops, (4) center cut pork chops, and (5) loin end or sirloin pork chops.

Although there are a variety of names for roasts derived from the regular pork loin, basically they are termed as rib end, rib half, loin end, loin half, or center cut roasts. These roasts may be bone-in or boneless.

Retailing

When pork loins arrive at the store, it is advisable to check the boxes and their contents for weight, type, and condition. In addition, quick, refrigerated storage of these loins is an important factor because pork is more perishable than beef or lamb and requires immediate attention. Pork loins are generally packaged in a corrugated box and, in handling these boxes from packing house to the retail store, pockets of warm air may form in the boxes. This may result in the formation of a film of moisture on the loins. If these loins are not

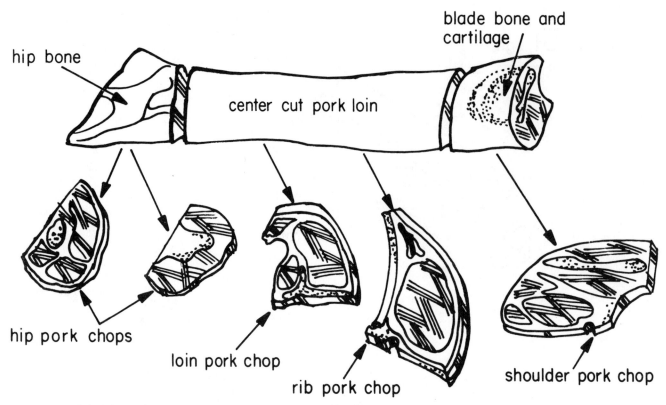

hip bone

blade bone and cartilage

center cut pork loin

hip pork chops

loin pork chop

rib pork chop

shoulder pork chop

FIG. 2.4. THESE ARE THE PORK CHOPS THAT COME FROM THE VARIOUS SECTIONS OF THE LOIN

going to be used for 1 or 2 days, it is important to wipe the moist surfaces from the loins.

Place the loins in the cooler immediately after delivery. Avoid leaving loins in cardboard cartons. It is best to remove loins from containers. Some meat coolers may not be properly refrigerated and the cold air may not penetrate through the cardboard carton. Place the loins on racks in the coldest area in the cooler with the bone side down. If they must be hung, it is advisable to insert the hook under the 1st rib bone. An experienced meat man will examine every pork loin to determine storage, use, cutting, and best merchandising cuts (chops, roasts, etc.). Meat coolers should maintain temperatures between 28° to 30°F. The relative humidity should be between 80 and 90% in order to control and prevent excessive shrinkage. A usual misconception is that meat will freeze at 32°F. Actually, meat will freeze at 27.5°F and not 32°F, because meat contains salt and other chemical components which reduce temperature at which it will freeze. It is advisable not to intermingle smoked pork products with fresh pork products. If cured products come in contact with fresh pork products, the fresh pork will lose some of its bloom. This is also true when displaying fresh and smoked pork products.

The most common type of pork loin sold to

retailers is a regular type loin called "14 lb and down." Although retailers would like to purchase extra trim and center cut loins, it would not be feasible because the difference in cost per pound would range between 18 and 20¢ per lb more than regular loins. This would demand a decided increase in the selling price and would cause the retailer to be custom, high-priced, rather than normally competitive. Most consumers are price conscious. In the metropolitan areas, multiethnic groups demand specific retail cuts derived from the pork loin. It is for this reason that certain retail cuts are sold in larger volume in one community and may do very poorly in other communities.

There are many factors that a retailer must take into consideration when purchasing loins. He must be aware of the advantages and disadvantages in purchasing extra trim, fancy, or center cuts. He should conduct cutting tests of his own to determine the best type of loin to purchase from packers and wholesalers. He should also compare packer prices on special cut loins as compared with the processing of these special cut loins that he does himself. The ethnic groups and customer preferences are very important factors to be considered before purchasing special types of pork loins. It has been suggested that these special types of loins should be purchased from packers. This is not always good practice because packers have different methods of processing them. Labor costs influence processing at the packing house and at the retail store. All retailers would like to keep their cost down as low as possible because of the keen competition in merchandising popular pork cuts.

When merchandising pork loins, the end cuts (shoulder end and loin end) are more complex to merchandise. This situation can be lessened if management varies the methods of merchandising described in this unit. Most meat cutters would like to sell these ends as roasts. This is not always feasible because of the many factors affecting merchandising such as the weather, time of year, cost factors, and related problems.

Before cutting the pork loin into chops, it is advisable to remove the skirt, the hanging tender, and the aorta (called the giblets), to facilitate trimming the chops. Because there may be a variety of pork loins packed in one box, some meat men will trim

the fat from some of the pork loins before cutting chops on the band saw. This practice is not generally advisable for the inexperienced meat cutter. The differences in the degree of meat in the loin eye muscle may cause the meat cutter to cut into the lean portion of the loin. A good meat merchandiser sorts the pork loins before cutting, so that the leaner-type loins are used first. The well-covered loins are generally used last because they keep better and do not discolor rapidly. This will be further discussed later in the unit. Some meat cutters will chill the pork loins by placing them in the freezer for a short period of time in order to make cutting the chops on the band saw easier. This practice is time-consuming and not advisable since moisture may collect in the package of chops and it may cause a wet-looking appearance which may discourage customer purchase. The procedures for cutting the entire loin into chops and the recommended suggestions for merchandising them follows.

Method No. 1

SLICING THE ENTIRE LOIN INTO CHOPS

1. Place the pork loin on the band saw with the backbone facing the cutting edge of the blade (see Fig. 2.5).

   Caution: Keep both hands and fingers clear from the path of the blade.

   Note: Some meat cutters prefer to cut the pork loin in half prior to cutting the chops (see Fig. 2.6).

2. Set the back plate gauge to the desired thickness. This may vary from ½ in. to ¾ in., depending upon store merchandising practices and customer preference. Cut the chops from the shoulder side first (blade end) or from the hip end first (loin end) depending upon whether the loin is a right- or left-sided loin.

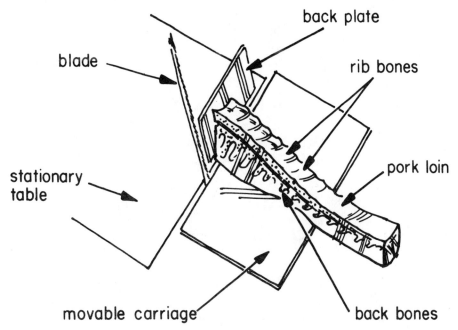

FIG. 2.5. POSITION OF LOIN FOR CUTTING CHOPS

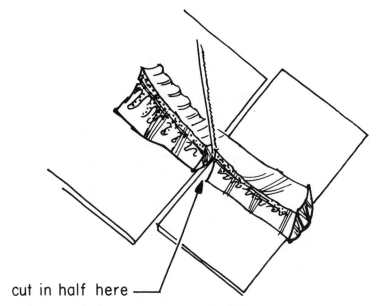

cut in half here ———

FIG. 2.6. SOMETIMES LOIN IS CUT IN HALF, AS SHOWN, BEFORE
CUTTING CHOPS

Caution: Do not force loin through blade; let the saw do the cutting. Use your
left hand to guide the sliced chop past the blade and then place the cut
chops on the stationary table (see Fig. 2.7).

Note: It is advisable to cut the ends from the pork loin first, leaving the center
for last. This will simplify cutting the last 2 or 3 chops of the loin and
prevent cutting a wedge-shaped chop (thick on one side and thin on the
other).

Caution: Always use the safety plate when cutting the last two chops.

3. Remove the bone dust from the chops and trim the chops in accordance with
store merchandising practices. This will vary from a ¼ to ½ in.

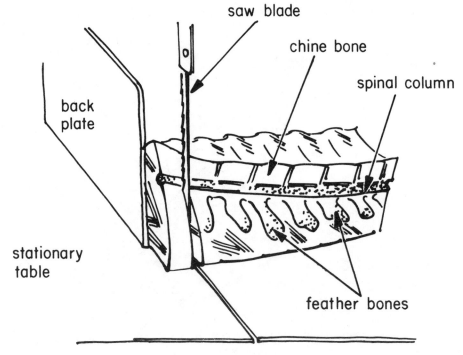

FIG. 2.7. CUT SHOULDER CHOPS FROM LOIN

Merchandising Practices for the Entire Loin

There are varying methods of merchandising pork chops from the pork loin which chain stores and supermarkets employ. Depending upon the weight of the loin and the thickness of the chops, there are approximately 30–36 chops cut from the average pork loin. Basically, there are 4–5 shoulder or blade chops (sometimes referred to as rib-end chops), 4–5 hip-end chops, sirloin-end chops (loin-end chops), and the remaining chops are generally called center cut pork chops (loin and rib). The names of these chops will vary from store to store.

It is not good practice to use only one method of packaging pork chops for display. It is advisable to use several forms of packaging to meet most consumer preferences even within one store. The 2-2-6 method has 2 shoulder chops, 2 hip chops, and 6 center cut chops all in one package. This is a package best suited for the large family. There usually remains approximately 10–12 center cut chops which are merchandised at a premium price (see Fig. 2.8). The 2-4 method generally will consist of 1 shoulder chop, 1 hip chop, and 4 center cut chops in one package (see Fig. 2.8). Other methods are often used to package the shoulder chops, or the hip chops, or a combination of shoulder and hip chops all in one package. The most common method of packaging center cut pork chops is six chops to a package (see Fig. 2.8). Some stores do not shingle (overlay) the chops as seen in Fig. 2.8, because they feel that they want the consumer to view the entire package of pork chops. They will use the flat type of package. There are differences of opinion regarding the eye appeal of the package. Shingled packages may make a more attractive-looking pack-

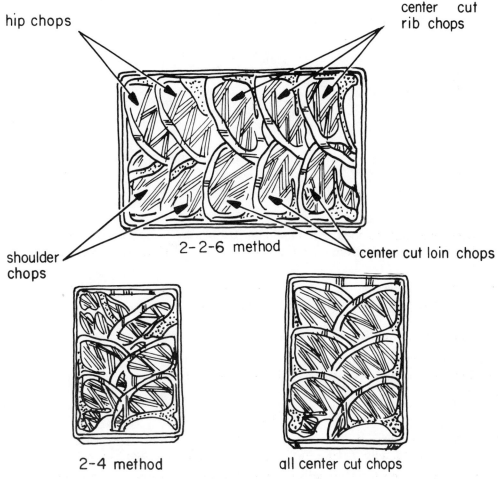

FIG. 2.8. PACKAGING TECHNIQUES FOR CHOPS

NOTE: Always place backbone at the outer edge of the boats.

age. Meat managers often instruct and check meat cutters so that packages containing 2–4 chops use the flat method, and anything over 4 chops use the shingled method.

Method No. 2

CUTTING SHOULDER, HIP END, AND CENTER CUT

1. To remove the shoulder end (blade end) from the pork loin, cut between the 3rd and 4th rib bone.

    Caution: Keep your fingers clear from the path of the blade.

    Note: Depending upon the weight and muscle structure of the pork loin, some meat cutters will cut between the 2nd and 3rd rib bone or the 4th and 5th rib bone. This will vary due to the weight range of the pork loin and in accordance with merchandising practices.

2. Remove the hip end (sirloin end) from the pork loin by cutting at the anterior end of the pelvic bone (in front of the hip bone).

    Note: The end of the pelvic bone is the general area where you can see the exposed portion of lean meat at the hip end as shown in Fig. 2.9. If the hip end is unevenly removed, simply correct by removing a chop from either end of the cut portion to even out the hip end.

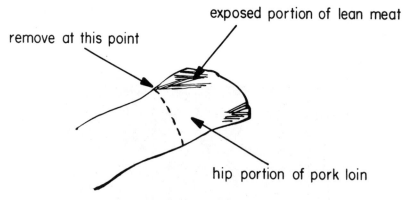

FIG. 2.9. REMOVE HIP END OF LOIN

3. After removing the ends, the remainder of the loin is now called a center cut loin. Cut the center into loin and rib chops to be merchandised as center cut pork chops.

    Note: It is advisable to remove some of the overlying meat and fat on the rib side of the center cut loin (see Fig. 2.10).

Merchandising Shoulder Ends from the Loin

The shoulder end (blade end) can be sliced into chops and merchandised as shoulder pork chops. If a variety of cuts is desired, employ either of the following methods.

Method A

1. Remove the blade portion or hinge the blade portion by cutting into the lean meat approximately ½ to 1 in. below the blade bone. (See Fig. 2.11.)

    Note: Some meat cutters will cut the shoulder end directly in half instead of ½ to 1 in. below the blade bone. This is a matter of store merchandising practices.

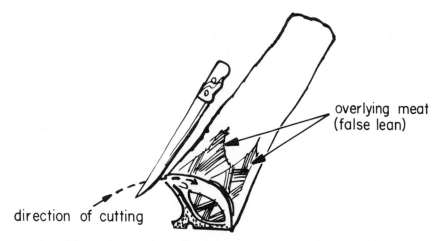

FIG. 2.10. REMOVE SOME OF THE OVERLYING MEAT AND FAT ON THE CENTER
CUT LOIN

2. Slice the hinged shoulder end portion into approximately 1 in. strips and place them in trays or boats with the meat side up. These are generally merchandised as "country-style spare ribs."

   Note: Some stores will remove the chine and feather bones prior to slicing the shoulder end. This will necessitate a higher price for country style spare ribs because some of the bones have been removed.

3. If the blade section is removed (instead of being hinged), follow the same procedure as in step No. 2 (see Fig. 2.11).

   Note: To facilitate cutting, it is advisable to slice the shoulder ends into 1-in. strips and then cut into the blade section and shoulder section for country style spare ribs (Fig. 2.11).

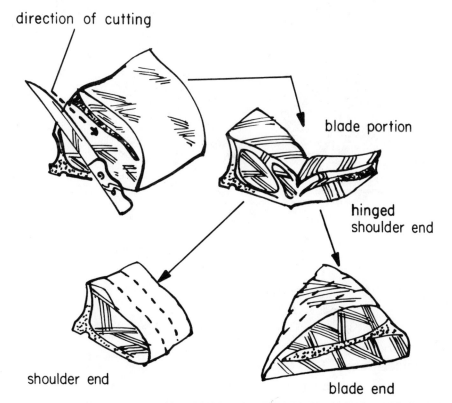

FIG. 2.11. COUNTRY STYLE SPARERIBS CAN BE MADE FROM SHOULDER (BLADE
END) OF LOIN

Method B

1. Remove the blade section of the shoulder end by cutting close to the underside of the blade bone (see Fig. 2.12A).

2. Remove the bone from the blade section and merchandise the meaty portion for a ground pork item such as pork patties, or grind in combination with beef and veal as a meat loaf item.

   Note: This boneless portion may also be put through the steak tenderizing machine with lean pork trimmings to make pork cube steaks.

3. Remove the chine and backbone on the band saw leaving approximately ½ in. of lean meat attached to the backbone (see Fig. 2.12B).

   Caution: Keep your fingers clear from the path of the blade. Place the flat surface of the shoulder end on the flat surface of the table.

   Note: The degree of meat left on the backbone will depend upon store merchandising practices. These bones can be merchandised as "backbone spare ribs."

4. Remove the loin back ribs by using the scalping method, cutting close to the rib bones leaving the finger meat between the rib bones (see Fig. 2.12C).

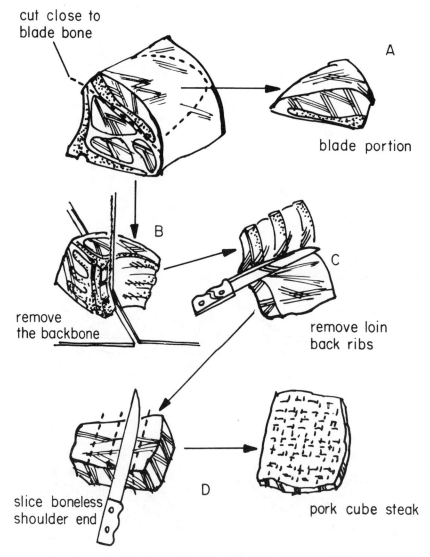

FIG. 2.12. SHOULDER (BLADE END) OF LOIN CAN BE MADE INTO PORK CUBE
STEAKS WITH BONED BLADE PORTION FOR GROUND PORK ITEMS

Note: These bones are merchandised as "loin back ribs" and the degree of meat on the bones will determine the price.

5. The remaining boneless shoulder pieces can be sliced into ½-in. slices and put through the steak tenderizing machine to make pork cube steaks (see Fig. 2.12D).

Note: These slices also may be mixed with the boneless blade section from step No. 2.

Note: This portion also may be cut into small cubes for boneless pork for chop suey or other similar dishes requiring cubed meats.

Merchandising Hip Ends (Sirloin Ends) from the Loin

The sirloin end (hip end) may be sliced into chops and merchandised as pork chops. These chops are known as hip pork chops. Retailers use varying methods of merchandising these ends. In most cases, store practices determine the method. Many meat men prefer to merchandise these ends as loin half or loin portion roasts. However, skill and knowledge are basic and important in applying the various methods in processing and merchandising the pork loin.

Some meat cutters prefer to bone hip ends and keep the bones devoid of any meat. The bones are either discarded or merchandised as pork bones. Some will leave a thick covering of meat on the bones, during the boning process. They are then retailed as country style ribs. This practice is not recommended because all the meat removed from the hip end can be merchandised at a higher retail selling price as a pork cutlet or a pork cube steak. Although there are variations in merchandising the boneless hip end, most of the time it is generally sold as pork cutlets. The reason for this is the fact that the meat is similar to a slice of fresh ham from the butt side of the ham, and it is practically devoid of all fat. The following is the suggested method for boning and merchandising hip ends.

Boning Procedure

1. Loosen and lay back the tenderloin muscle, and a small portion of the flank edge by cutting close to the chine bone and following the contour of the bone (see Fig. 2.13).

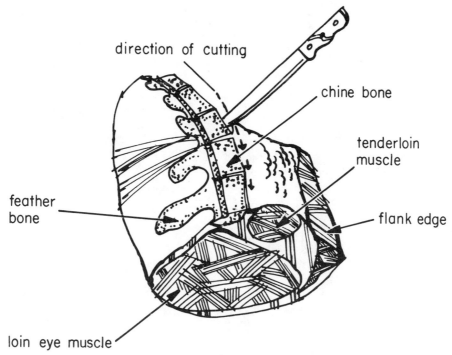

FIG. 2.13. LOIN VIEW OF HIP END

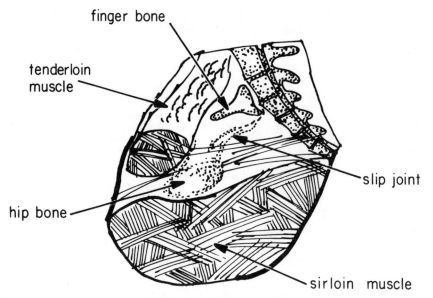

FIG. 2.14. SIRLOIN VIEW OF LOIN HIP END

Caution: Keep your free hand behind the cutting action of the knife.

Note: This will expose the slip joint between the hip and tail bone. Do not attempt to cut through this joint. Your knife may slip and cause an injury.

2. Continue to cut around the end of the hip bone, following the contour of the bone, and free the meat from the hip, tail, and feather bones (see Fig. 2.14).

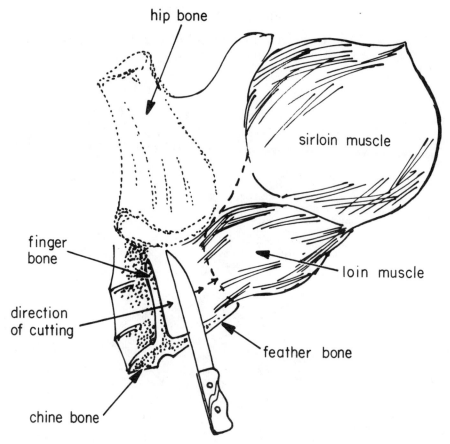

FIG. 2.15. FREE THE MEAT FROM THE HIP END OF THE LOIN

Caution: Cut away from the body and down to the bench.

Note: Some meat cutters may or may not remove the meat between the finger bone and hip bone. This is a matter of store policy and practice. If this meat is removed, and it should be, this portion can be used for a ground pork or pork cube steak item. (See Fig. 2.15.)

Merchandising Procedure

Basically, the boneless hip end consists of three distinct muscles: the sirloin muscle, the strip loin, and the tenderloin muscle. The most important muscle is the sirloin muscle because of the high percentage of lean. It is generally sliced into pork cutlets. Pork cutlets should be sliced approximately 1/16-in. in thickness or even thinner, as required. Try to avoid pounding the meat with a cleaver or wooden mallet. This is poor practice. A good meat cutter should have no difficulty in slicing meat thin. When meat is flattened with a heavy object, the cell walls are broken and this causes the juices to flow more freely from the meat, thus more flavor is lost.

1. The tenderloin muscle from the hip end is very small and should be sliced or cubed depending upon customer specifications or store practices. (See Fig. 2.16.)

   Note: Remove the excess fat.

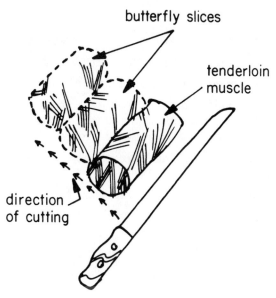

FIG. 2.16. SLICE TENDERLOIN MUSCLE FROM THE HIP END

2. The sirloin muscle should be sliced thin for pork cutlets. (See Fig. 2.17.)

   Note: These meaty slices can also be mixed with various pork trimmings (such as blade meat) and put through a steak tenderizing machine to make a pork cube steak.

It is important to be aware of the fact that merchandising boneless pork hip ends will vary from region to region of the country. They will also vary within the same chain and within the same community. There are no set patterns for merchandising. They will depend upon many factors such as the type of pork loin from which the hip was derived, the price factor, the season of year that may affect cooking preferences, and the consumers' demands. It is important that the skill and knowledge of the meat cutter be used efficiently to maintain good volume and satisfy customer preferences. For further reference, a recommended source of various retail cuts obtained from the pork loin is published in a manual by The National Livestock and Meat Board entitled *Merchandising Pork Loins.*

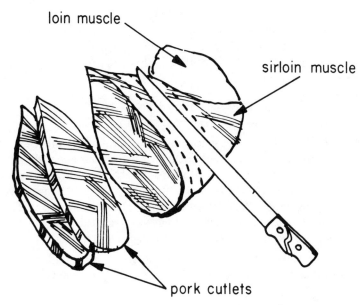

FIG. 2.17. SLICE CUTLETS FROM SIRLOIN MUSCLE

Method No. 3
CUTTING RIB PORTION, LOIN PORTION, AND CENTER CUT LOIN ROASTS

1. To remove the rib portion from the loin, cut between the 7th and 8th rib bone.

   Caution: Keep your fingers clear from the path of the blade.

   Note: Because of the wide variety of pork loins, some meat cutters will cut very large pork loins between the 5th and 6th, or the 6th and 7th rib bone, depending upon the desired weight of the roast.

2. Cut between the rib bones cutting through the chine and feather bones (backbone). (See Fig. 2.18.)

   Caution: Care should be taken not to catch or snag the back of the blade while removing the cut backbone from the path of the blade. This may

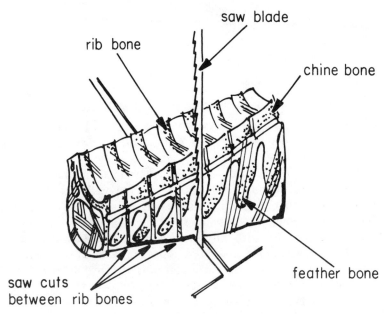

FIG. 2.18. SAW THROUGH BACKBONE ON THE BAND SAW

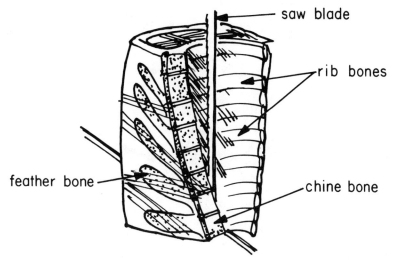

FIG. 2.19. OR SAW THROUGH AT THE BASE OF THE RIB BONES

cause the blade to slip off the wheel of the bandsaw and create a loud startling noise alarming the meat cutter. This may cause an accident.

Note: The above operation can also be performed with a hand saw.

Note: Some meat cutters will also cut through the blade bone, depending on how large a portion of the blade bone remains in the pork loin.

3. Another method of cutting through the bones in order to make carving the pork loin roast easier after cooking is to place the pork loin on its shoulder end flat with the table top and then saw through at the base of the rib bones (see Fig. 2.19).

Note: Do not remove the bone. Simply cut through to loosen the meat from the bone, leaving the bone attached to the roast. Some meat cutters may leave the bone in one piece or cut the backbone in 2 or 3 pieces and then tie the backbone to the roast. This is a matter of store merchandising practices (see Fig. 2.20).

4. Remove loin portion by cutting approximately 7 in. from the loin end or 2 in. from the end of the hip bone.

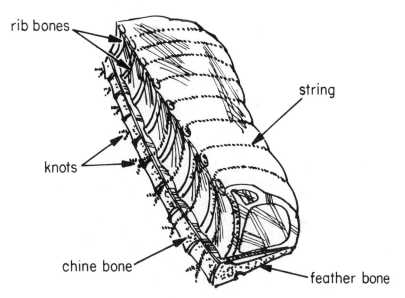

FIG. 2.20. TIE LOOSENED BACKBONE BACK ON ROAST

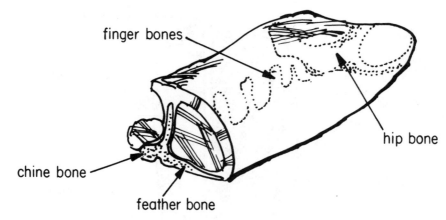

FIG. 2.21. VIEW OF LOIN PORTION OF ROAST

Note: Some chain stores and supermarkets require their meat cutters to include a minimum of 2 in. of the center cut from the end of the hip bone. The exact amount of loin portion to remove from the loin is generally governed by store merchandising practices.

5. To crack the backbone on the loin portion of the pork roast, it is advisable to cut through the backbone at the cartilage junction on the chine bone. This will assist the consumer in slicing the loin roast after it is cooked, because the finger bones located in the loin muscle are centered between each vertebrae. (See Fig. 2.21).

Caution: Do not cut too deep on the backbone portion of the roast. Try to cut deep into the hip bone to assist the housewife in slicing the cooked roast (see Fig. 2.22).

Note: Some chain stores and supermarkets instruct their meat cutters to cut a loin portion roast so that it weighs approximately ⅓ of the weight of the loin. This may also vary from store to store, depending upon merchandising practice and consumer preference.

6. Because of the large demand for center cut pork chops, it is not advisable to prepare center cut loin roasts unless, of course, the consumer demands it. If center cut roasts are prepared, simply cut through the backbone at each cartilage junc-

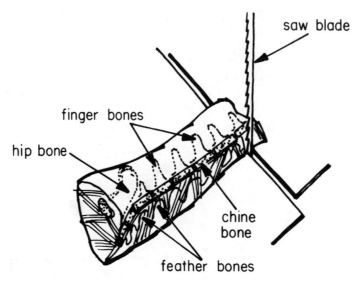

FIG. 2.22. SAW THROUGH THE BACKBONE ON THE LOIN PORTION

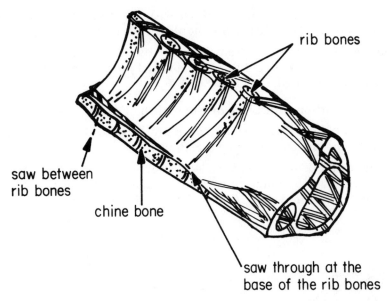

FIG. 2.23. VIEW OF CENTER CUT PORK LOIN ROAST

tion or saw through at the base of the rib bones across the entire length of the roast (see Fig. 2.23).

Merchandising Note: Because of keen competition, it is advisable not to remove any of the chine bone or surface fat. This would cause the item to be merchandised at a higher retail selling price.

Method No. 4
BONING THE RIB PORTION AND LOIN PORTION OF LOIN ROASTS
Rib Portion

1. Remove the blade section (blade bone and overlying meat) by cutting close to the underside of the blade bone. (See Fig. 2.24.)

Caution: Keep fingers behind the cutting action of the knife.

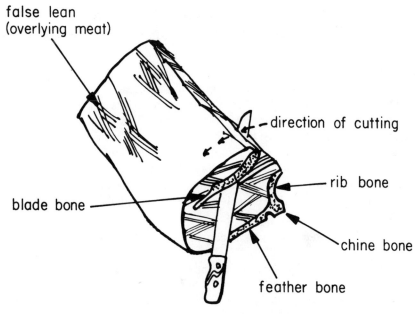

FIG. 2.24. REMOVE THE BLADE BONE AND FALSE LEAN

Note: This section can be merchandised with the bone-in or boneless. Refer to the section on merchandising shoulder ends (method No. 2).

2. The amount of feather bones remaining on the rib portion of the loin depends upon how the carcass was split during the initial processing. Either of the following methods may be used.

Portion with Little or None of the Feather Bones

1. Remove the rib bones by keeping the knife close to the rib bones and cutting down toward the chine bone. (See Fig. 2.25.)

    Note: This method of boning is called "scalping." Some retailers may or may not remove the chine bone prior to merchandising these bones as loin back ribs. The degree of meat left on the bones will depend upon store merchandising practices.

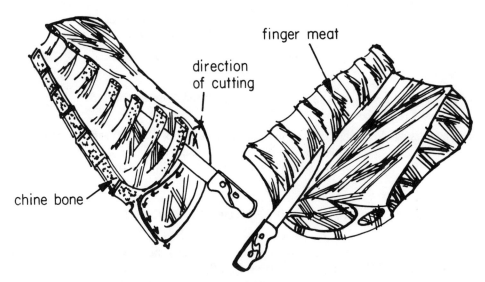

FIG. 2.25. SCALP THE RIB BONES FROM THE RIB PORTION

Portion with the Backbone Left Intact

1. Remove the backbone (chine and feather bone) by cutting through at the base of the rib bone.

    Caution: Keep fingers clear from the path of the blade.
    Note: This procedure can also be done with a handsaw.
    Note: The degree of meat left on the backbone is a matter of merchandising practice. Some retailers will leave as much as 1 in. of meat on the backbone and merchandise these bones as "backbone spareribs." Other retailers do not leave any meat on the backbone and merchandise these bones as pork bones. They may also mix them with neck bones. Still other retailers feel that all the meat should remain on the boneless roast because of the high retail sales value. Again, this is a matter of store merchandising practices.

2. Remove the rib bones by using the scalping method as described above. (See Fig. 2.25.)

3. Place opposite ends of the boneless rib portion facing each other, so that they are equal in circumference (round shape). The inside cut surfaces are now facing each other. Place one guide string to hold both roasts together; then tie cross strings approximately two fingers apart for a uniform roast (see Fig. 2.26).

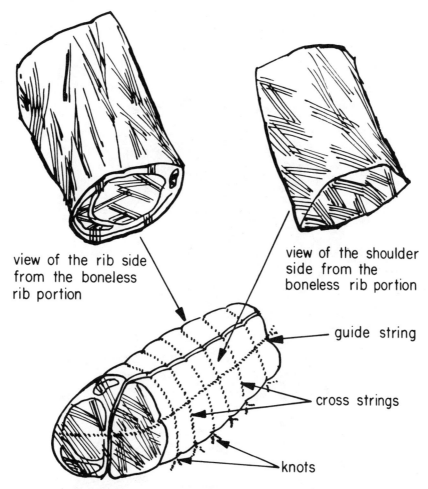

view of the rib side
from the boneless
rib portion

view of the shoulder
side from the
boneless rib portion

guide string

cross strings

knots

FIG. 2.26. TWO BONELESS RIB PORTIONS, AS SHOWN, TIED TOGETHER FOR A
ROAST

Note: Some meat cutters may use three boneless rib portions tied together. This is an unusual store merchandising practice. Consumers are aware of the fact that pork must be thoroughly cooked. Try to keep the circumference of the roast small. The larger the circumference of the roast, the more time will be required to cook the roast thoroughly. Time is often important to the housewife.

Loin Portion

1. Loosen and lay back the tenderloin muscle by cutting close to the chine bone and down to the finger bones. This will expose the tips of the finger bones (see Fig. 2.27).

   Note: Leave the tenderloin muscle attached to the loin. Do not remove the tenderloin muscle. This may cause some difficulty when tieing the roast.

2. Loosen all the meat from the hip bone and cut down toward the tips of the finger bones to complete the operation. (See Fig. 2.28.)

   Caution: Keep your fingers behind the cutting section of the knife.

3. The boneless loin portion may be tied as a single roast, or place opposite ends from two boneless loin portions facing each other. Tie the cross strings approximately two fingers apart. (See Fig. 2.26.)

   Note: Some meat cutters will remove the tenderloin muscle before tieing the roast. This is not advisable. Before merchandising the tenderloin muscle

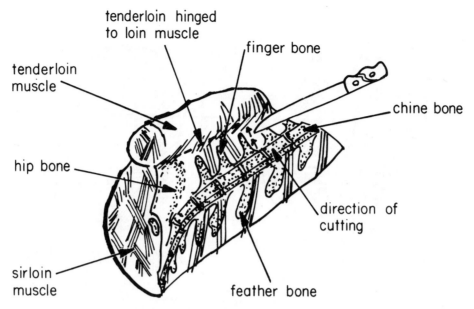

FIG. 2.27. LOOSEN TENDERLOIN MUSCLE

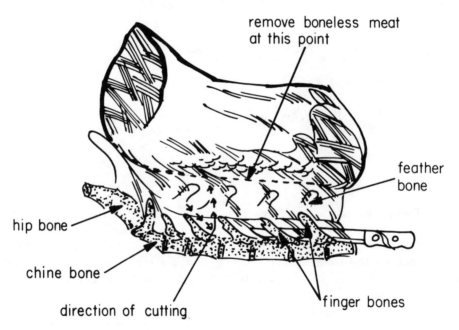

FIG. 2.28. REMOVE BACKBONE FROM THE LOIN PORTION

in any form, it must be trimmed close to the membrane. If the tenderloin muscle is left intact with the roast, no further trimming is necessary. The fat remaining will dissolve during the cooking process and will produce a more flavorful roast.

Method No. 5

RIB HALF AND LOIN HALF

Many chain stores, supermarkets, and independent retail stores will vary procedures when cutting the rib half and the loin half from the pork loin. Basically, a loin half from the pork loin should include at least 1 rib bone. The remainder is called the rib half. This is actually not a true half because the rib half will represent approximately 55–60% of the loin, and the loin half will represent approximately

40–45% of the loin. A true half from the pork loin should be cut to include approximately 3 to 4 ribs on the loin side of the half, or until both sides are of equal weight. Some meat cutters will remove 4 to 6 chops from the center of the loin and then retail the two remaining pieces as a rib half and a loin half. This is a matter of store merchandising practice.

To prepare the rib half and the loin half for pork loin roasts (bone-in or boneless) follow the same procedures in method No. 3 or No. 4 (rib portion and loin portion). The only difference is the fact that the pork loin is cut in half.

Method No. 6

SPECIALTY ITEMS FROM PORK LOINS

The majority of all the specialty cuts which are derived from the pork loin are a matter of store merchandising practices and customer request. These specialties are not often available in chain stores and supermarkets because of the increased labor costs due to the time, the skill, and knowledge required in the production of these specialty cuts. Supervisors and managers are interested in increasing volume, which reduces operating expenses with increased amounts of meat sold. These facts will be further developed in units to follow. Many retail stores and prime shops will feature this type of specialty cutting because the chains and supermarkets do not compete in this area. Therefore, it is important to acquire the cutting skills and knowledge in processing these specialty cuts.

I. Crown Roasts

Although there are variations in the preparation of crown roasts, the basic concept is to form the roast into a circle to resemble a King's crown. It is advisable to use the center cut loins from the rib side containing approximately 6–7 rib bones, and with the least amount of backbone, in order to form a more perfect circle. Crown roasts are prepared with the bone in, semiboneless, or completely boneless. A simple method follows.

1. Select two center cut loins of approximately the same length (see Fig. 2.29).

    Note: Because of the variations in size of loins in a packing box, try to keep the rib bones of each cut approximately the same in height.

2. Crack the chine and backbone by sawing between each rib bone on the band saw.

    Caution: Do not cut too deep or you will score the meat and cause the shape of roast to be irregular. (See Fig. 2.29.)

    Note: This operation can also be done with a hand saw.

3. Remove all the meat above the rib eye muscle across the length of both loins. Scrape the rib bone ends free from meat and fat as in Fig. 2.30.

    Note: The reason for exposing the ends of the rib bones is to make possible the dressing up of the roast with paper frills, attached or covering the rib ends.

4. Stitch the ends of the pork loin by tieing the two end rib bones together to form a circle. (See Fig. 2.31.)

    Note: Some meat cutters prefer to remove the chine and backbone by sawing across the length of the roast at the base of the rib bones in order to form a better circle of meat. The bone removal and weight loss that results will necessarily increase the selling price of the crown roast. Bone removal may also cause shrinkage during the cooking process. The price factor is, therefore, important and must be given careful consideration when merchandising.

II. French Roasts

This type of roast is similar to the crown roast except that it is not shaped into a circle. (Refer to Fig. 2.30.)

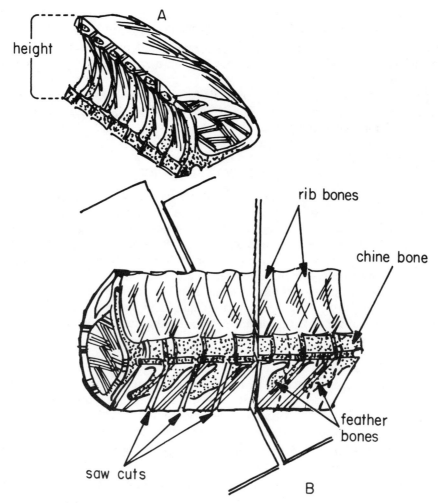

FIG. 2.29. (A) SELECT TWO CENTER CUT PORK LOINS OF EQUAL HEIGHT AND
(B) CRACK BACKBONES, AS SHOWN

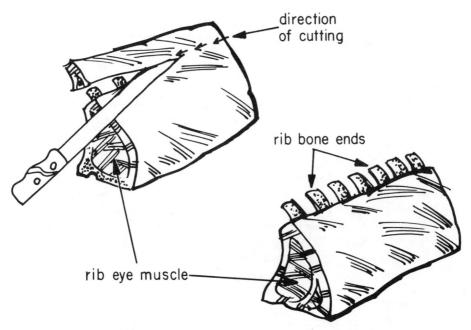

FIG. 2.30. REMOVE MEAT FROM RIBS ABOVE THE RIB EYE MUSCLE

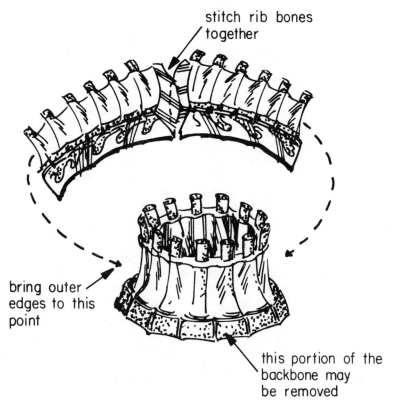

FIG. 2.31. FINAL STEPS IN MAKING A CROWN ROAST

1. Select a center cut loin with approximately 5–7 ribs.
2. Follow steps No. 2 and No. 3 in the preparation of a crown roast.

   Note: The chine bone can be cut lengthwise across the base of the rib bones, or between each rib bone.

III. Pan Fry Pork Chops (Quick Fries)

1. Chops are cut from the center cut and may be either rib or loin, but must be cut thin. These chops are generally ½-in. in thickness.

   Note: Thickness will depend upon store merchandising practices and consumer request. These chops generally return a higher price.

IV. French Rib Pork Chops

1. Cut the center cut chops from the rib side of the loin. Cut chops approximately 1-in. thick. Remove about 1 in. from the top portion of the rib bone.

   Note: It is advisable to remove the meat from the top portion of the rib bones while the loin is in one piece. This will save time.

   Note: This type of chop may also be retailed as a stuffed pork chop by merely placing a pocket in the chop.

V. Stuffed Pork Chops

1. Chops may be cut from the rib or loin from the center cut pork loin. Cut the chops about 1-in. thick.
2. Place a pocket in the chop from the top portion of the chop.

   Note: Try to keep the opening as small as possible to prevent stuffing from seeping out during the cooking process.

UNIT 3: Pork Shoulders

Pork shoulders consist of two wholesale cuts which are (1) the fresh shoulder picnic, and (2) the fresh shoulder Boston butt. Shoulders are generally referred to as a regular pork shoulder or a New York shoulder. Modern packers rarely cut regular pork shoulders because of decreasing demand for this type of cut. Retailers can now purchase Boston butts and fresh picnics and merchandise them without further cutting or processing of these wholesale cuts. This eliminates some of the labor costs and provides for more efficient cutting of these wholesale cuts into retail cuts which are more popular. This unit will deal with the two wholesale cuts, the picnic and the butt, and their relationship to processing and merchandising methods.

See Fig. 3.1 and examine the region of the pork carcass from which the pork shoulder is cut. When shoulders are removed from the carcass, packers generally refer to them as untrimmed shoulders because of the attached neck bones, clear plate, front feet, and knuckles. All of these parts must be removed. The untrimmed shoulder is removed from the pork carcass side by cutting between the 2nd and 3rd rib bone and removing the jowl close to the exposed end of the atlas bone. (See Fig. 3.2.) The untrimmed shoulder is then processed further into a fresh picnic and a Boston butt by removing the neck bone, front foot, portion of breast meat (breast flap) from the picnic, and separating the picnic from the butt by cutting at the neck portion of the blade bone (see Fig. 3.1). Some packers re-move ⅔ of the rind from the butt end. The clear plate is then trimmed from the Boston butt.

Packers will process various types of fresh shoulder picnics in accordance with purchaser's demands and specifications, as they will fit in with the packer's production practices. Short-shank picnics are regular type picnics. The shank is cut off approximately 1–2 in. from the arm pit and parallel to the knee (cappal) joint (refer to Fig. 3.1). The shankless picnic has the shanks removed close to the breast bone or near the joint of the shank and arm bone (arm bone socket). The picnics are then trimmed according to packer specifications (removal of some rind and fat) and placed into cardboard cartons in accordance with weight ranges. These ranges may vary from 4 to 6 lb, 6 to 8 lb, and 8 to 12 lb. Packers generally pack Boston butts in the same manner as fresh picnics.

Some meat men may refer to the fresh shoulder picnic as a Cala ham. This term is incorrect and barred by law in many states because the term "ham" misrepresents the cut. Consumers usually refer to cala or picnic as a cured and smoked product.

Refer to Fig. 3.1 and examine the bone structure of the picnic and the butt. Of the two wholesale cuts, the less desirable cut to most consumers is the picnic. This is due to the amount of bone and fat contained in the picnic. The following are some suggested methods for merchandising the picnic and the butt.

MERCHANDISING THE FRESH SHOULDER PICNIC (SHANKLESS)

It is advisable for meat retailers to purchase fresh shoulder picnics with the shank removed (shankless). This will eliminate labor costs and produce a better finished product for the consumer. Shanks can be purchased separately from packers, if needed. This topic will be further developed in subsequent units on pork. To achieve greater tonnage in the merchandising of pork products, it would be advisable to purchase fresh shoulder picnics in the various weight ranges, keeping in mind the following rules of thumb regarding the merchandising of fresh picnics:

4–6 lb range: merchandise whole with bone in or boneless
6–8 lb range: merchandise whole or half with bone in or boneless
8–12 lb range: merchandise whole, half, or sliced with bone in or boneless

Boning the Fresh Shoulder Picnic (Shankless) (Tunneling Method)

Wherever possible, try to avoid boning by cutting through the lean meat to re-move the bones. If you are not already doing so, learn to use the tunnel method

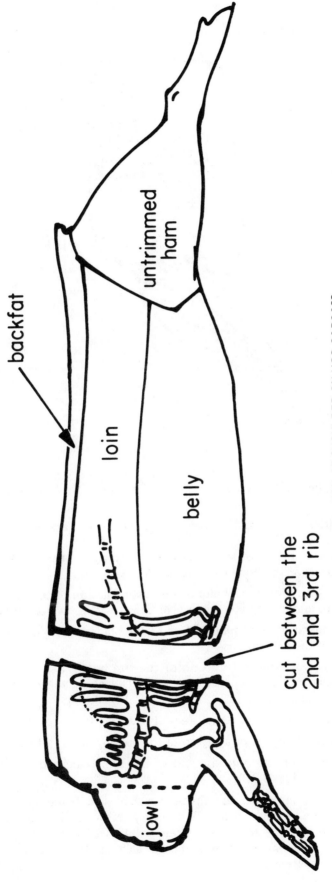

backfat

loin

untrimmed ham

belly

cut between the 2nd and 3rd rib

jowl

FIG. 3.1. LOCATION OF SHOULDER ON HOG CARCASS
This is the appearance of the untrimmed shoulder.

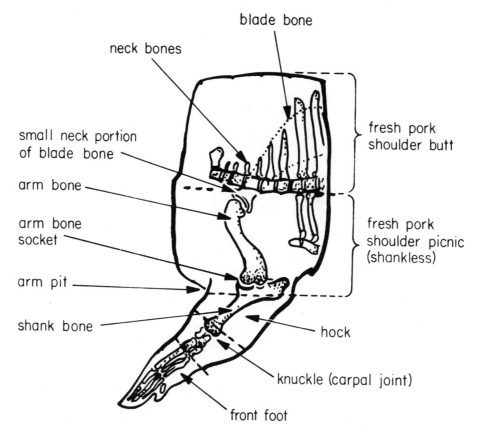

FIG. 3.2. BONE STRUCTURE OF AN UNTRIMMED PORK SHOULDER

because it makes slicing the cooked roast easier and with more appealing sliced portions.

1. Place the shoulder on the bench with the rind side down and lean portion facing up. (See Fig. 3.3.)

2. Remove the socket portion of the blade bone, keeping the tip of the boning knife against the contour of the bone (see Fig. 3.3A).

   Caution: Keep your free hand behind the cutting action of the knife. Use small strokes and always cut down. Never cut with upward strokes.

   Note: After removal of the small portion of the blade bone, you can see the ball portion of the arm bone.

3. Loosen the meat from the ball portion of the arm bone. Use the tip of the boning knife, keeping the knife against the bone. Cut along the bone as far as you can reach without scoring the inside muscle (see Fig. 3.3B).

   Note: Knowledge of the bone structure is always helpful in removing bones.

   Caution: Keep your finger tips away from the cutting action of the knife.

4. Loosen the meat from the opposite end of the arm bone and remove the bone from either end (see Fig. 3.3C).

   Note: The manner in which the shank was removed from the fresh shoulder picnic at the packing plant will determine how much of the shank bone is left attached to the arm bone. There will be variations from one packer to another. The boneless fresh picnic can also be merchandised as a specialty stuffed meat item.

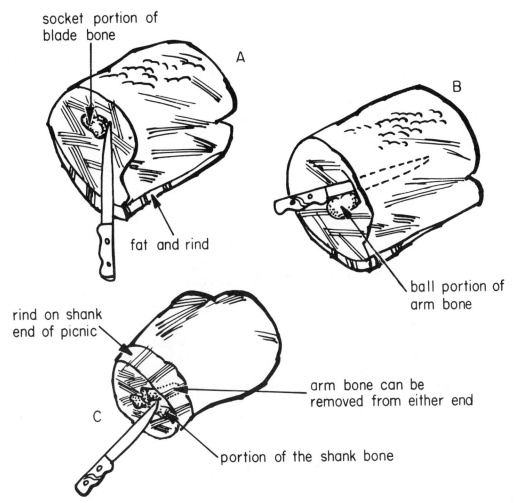

socket portion of
blade bone

A

B

fat and rind

ball portion of
arm bone

rind on shank
end of picnic

C

arm bone can be
removed from either end

portion of the shank bone

FIG. 3.3. TO BONE A FRESH SHOULDER PICNIC (SHANKLESS): (A) REMOVE SOCKET PORTION
OF BLADE BONE; (B) LOOSEN MEAT FROM BALL PORTION OF ARM BONE; (C) REMOVE THE ARM
BONE

Tieing the Boneless Fresh Picnic

1. Place a stitch with the needle to close the cavity at the shank end of the picnic at
   the point the bone was removed (see Fig. 3.4A).
2. Place one or two guide strings lengthwise around the picnic (see Fig. 3.4B).
3. Tie evenly-spaced cross strings. It is advisable to start the cross strings at the butt
   end of the picnic to form a better rolled and shaped picnic. This will tend to
   keep the cut surface even (see Fig. 3.4C).

   Note: If the twine slides from its position, a small scoring cut on the rind will
   hold the twine in position. Refer to notes on tieing fresh ham roasts in
   Unit 4.

Cutting the Picnic into Slices and Halves

It is not advisable to remove slices from a fresh shoulder picnic weighing from 6
to 8 lb. These picnics should only be cut in half. This cut is a better buy for small
families. It is advisable to use the fresh shoulder picnics in the weight range of 8 to
12 lb for slicing purposes. The principal reason for this merchandising method is the
fact that the slices removed from smaller picnics, or the entire picnic, will not sell as
readily as center slices. Center cut slices resemble fresh ham slices. The slices toward the shank end are generally tougher as well as smaller. This may discourage

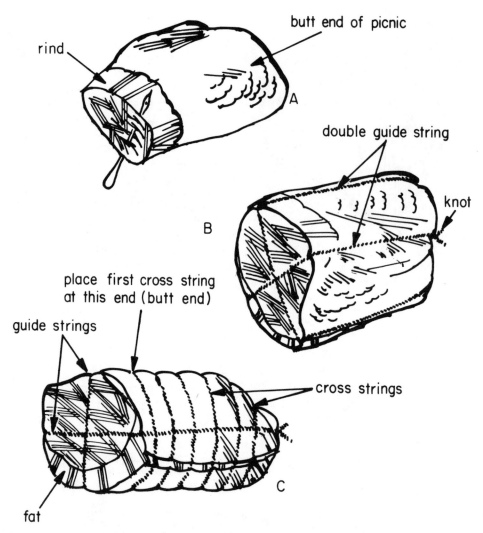

FIG. 3.4. TO TIE A FRESH BONELESS SHOULDER PICNIC: (A) PLACE TWO STITCHES TO
CLOSE CAVITY; (B) PLACE A DOUBLE GUIDE STRING, AS SHOWN, AROUND THE PICNIC;
(C) THEN PLACE CROSS STRINGS TO SECURE SHAPE, AS SHOWN

customers from purchasing picnics. This may also have a negative effect upon the
sales tonnage of fresh pork products. A satisfied customer is perhaps the best adver-
tising source for increased and repeat sales. The following are suggested methods for
the cutting of fresh shoulder picnics.

Cutting the Picnic In Half

1. Place the picnic on the band saw with the rind side toward the table.
2. Estimate approximately a 1/2 cut parallel to the cut surface of the butt end (see
   Fig. 3.5).

   Note: After cutting, it is advisable to inform the wrappers to keep the clear film
   wrap on the cut surface and on the lean surface. Place the ends of film
   wrap on the rind or fat side of the cut picnic halves. This will make for a
   more attractive cut of meat.

Cutting the Picnic Into Butt and Shank Portions, and Center Cut Slices

1. Remove approximately 1/3 of the fresh shoulder from the butt end (refer back to
   Fig. 3.5).

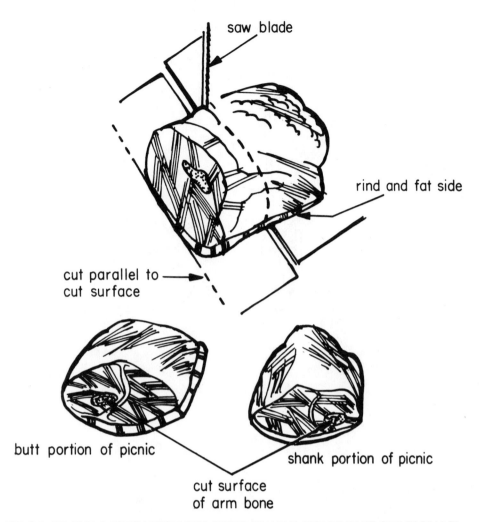

saw blade

rind and fat side

cut parallel to cut surface

butt portion of picnic

shank portion of picnic

cut surface
of arm bone

FIG. 3.5. TO CUT A FRESH SHOULDER PICNIC IN HALF, CUT ON BAND SAW PARALLEL
TO THE CUT SURFACE OF THE SHOULDER WHICH WILL GIVE THE BUTT PORTION AND
THE SHANK PORTION OF THE PICNIC

Note: This portion should be about 3–4 lb in weight. Avoid cutting smaller units which may not be merchandised readily. Such leftover cuts must be re-trimmed, rewrapped, or reprocessed into other cuts which are very costly and time-consuming.

2. Cut 3 to 4 slices from the cut surface of the shank end. The thickness of these steaks will vary from $\frac{1}{2}$ to $\frac{3}{4}$ in. The actual thickness is a matter of store merchandising practice. (See Fig. 3.6.)

   Note: Remove the bone dust from both sides and place the slices in appropriate boat containers. These slices can then be merchandised as fresh shoulder picnic steaks.

3. The remainder of the picnic, which should be approximately $\frac{1}{3}$ of the original weight, can then be merchandised as the shank portion of the fresh shoulder picnic.

MERCHANDISING THE FRESH SHOULDER (BOSTON BUTT)

Chain stores and supermarkets generally merchandise fresh butts either in their whole form or cut in half. There are numerous cuts which can be used to increase the tonnage of pork without further increasing the cost of labor. A good meat cutter should be skilled and knowledgeable in determining the parts used for different retail cuts and how these cuts may be used for cooking various pork

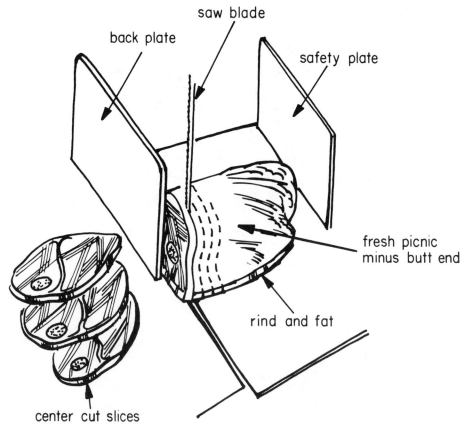

FIG. 3.6. CENTER CUTS MAY BE SLICED FROM A FRESH SHOULDER PICNIC

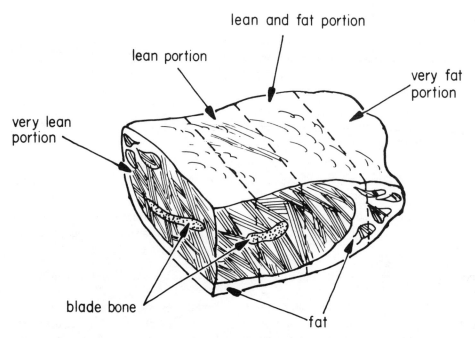

FIG. 3.7. SHOWING THE LEAN, FAT, AND BONE STRUCTURE OF A FRESH SHOULDER
BUTT (BOSTON)

dishes. Butts, generally, can be merchandised whole, cut in half, sliced, cubed, or ground. Methods will vary among meat cutters, but a good meat cutter will understand the muscle structure of the butt and thereby be better able to cut and process the butt properly. The muscle structure of the butt will change with every slice removed from the butt. The intermingling fat increases toward the end of the butt. (See Fig. 3.7.)

Butts are generally packed and shipped from the packer in cartons with weight ranges from 4 to 6 lb, 6 to 8 lb, and 8 to 12 lb. Boxes and cartons will average in weight from 30 to 50 lb, depending upon the packer and the amount specified by the purchaser. On the eastern coast of the United States, especially in the New York area, retail meat men refer to butts as a Western butt or a City butt. Meat cutters will generally refer to the differences between the two by indicating that the City butts are leaner than the Western butts. Some packers in the midwest have different packer names for butts such as lean, regular, or fancy type with the difference being in the amount of fat remaining on the butt. Some mix various sizes and types within the same box. A good meat cutter and merchandiser will sort the butts when they arrive to see which should be merchandised as roasts, steaks, cutlets, or cubed for various menu dishes. Use the lean type of butt for slices and cubed retail cuts. Use the fatter types for roasts.

Boning the Fresh Shoulder Butt (Boston)

1. Place the butt on the bench with the fat surface facing the bench.

   Note: The exposed view of the blade bone on both sides is now facing you.

2. Cut through the lean so that the tip of the boning knife will cut directly on the flat surface of the blade bone. (See Fig. 3.8A.)

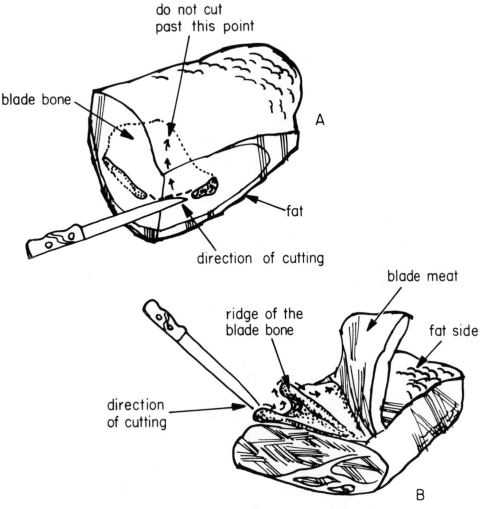

FIG. 3.8. TO BONE THE BOSTON BUTT: (A) LOOSEN MEAT FROM THE FLAT SURFACE OF THE BLADE BONE AND (B) REMOVE BLADE BONE

Caution: Keep your free hand behind the cutting action of the knife.

Note: Remove the lean from the bone only to the outer edge of the bone. Try to avoid scoring deeper into the butt.

3. Reverse the butt so that the fat surface is facing up. Cut above the blade bone and around the ridge, and free the bone from the butt (see Fig. 3.8B).

Caution: Use the tip of the boning knife against the bone to catch the seam, if possible.

Note: Do not discard these bones as they can be merchandised as pork bones. Many consumers of various ethnic groups use these bones for flavor in various specialty dishes.

Tying the Boneless Butt

1. Place one guide string around the length of the butt to secure the blade portion of the butt (see Fig. 3.9A).

Note: Some meat cutters will place one or two stitches to secure the blade meat with the butt. This is a matter of store practice. Some stores may even remove the entire blade section and merchandise the blade meat separately.

2. Place evenly-spaced cross strings, starting at the blade section first, to secure an even surface (see Fig. 3.9B).

Note: Place all knots to one side of the butt so that the completed roll can be viewed by the customer from the lean surface or the fat surface, depending upon store merchandising practices. Try to keep the knots in a fairly straight line (see Fig. 3.9B). Large size butts can be cut in half and

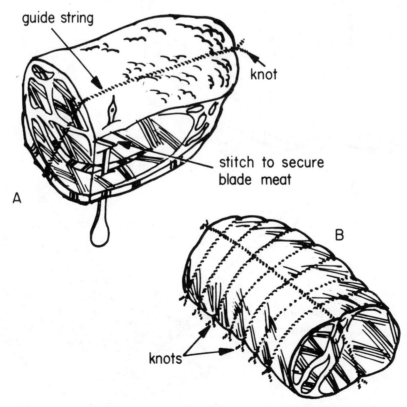

FIG. 3.9. TO TIE THE BONELESS BOSTON BUTT: (A) FIRST STITCH TO SE-
CURE BLADE MEAT AND PLACE GUIDE STRING END-TO-END AROUND BUTT;
(B) THEN SECURE SHAPE BY CROSS STRINGS, KNOTTING AT BASE OF BUTT

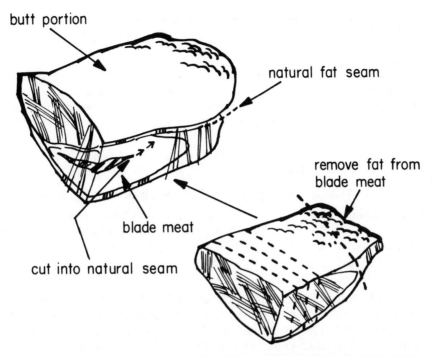

butt portion

natural fat seam

remove fat from
blade meat

blade meat

cut into natural seam

FIG. 3.10. BLADE MEAT ALSO MAY BE REMOVED FROM BOSTON BUTT WHICH
CAN THEN BE USED TO MAKE PORK CUBE STEAKS, SLICED FOR BUTTERFLIED
CUTLETS, OR MIXED WITH FAT TRIMMINGS AND GROUND FOR PORK PATTIES

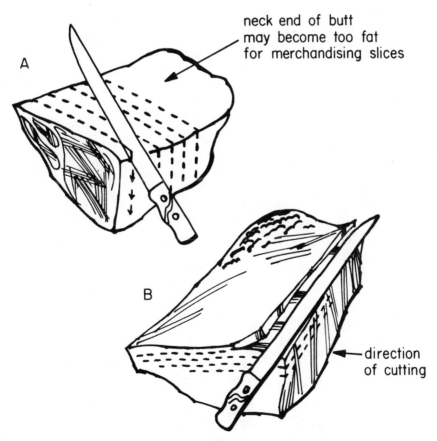

A

neck end of butt
may become too fat
for merchandising slices

B

direction
of cutting

FIG. 3.11. THE REMAINDER (BUTT PORTION) OF THE BONELESS BOSTON BUTT
MAY BE SLICED: CUT THIN SLICES EITHER CROSSWISE (A) OR LENGTHWISE (B)

sold as two roasts which may fit the needs of consumers with small families.

Slicing the Fresh Shoulder Butt (Bone-In)

It is advisable to slice butts only past the blade bone. It is impractical to slice a butt to the very end because of the intermingling fat at the end. Slice only half of the butt and the remaining half can be merchandised as a roast. (Refer back to Fig. 3.7.)

Slicing the Fresh Shoulder Butt (Boneless)

Some meat men refer to the boneless butt as the "heart" of the butt.

1. Separate the blade meat from the butt at the natural fat seam (see Fig. 3.10).
2. Basically, there are two methods for slicing the butt portion into thin slices approximately $\frac{1}{8}$ to $\frac{1}{4}$ in. thick to be merchandised as pork cutlets (see Fig. 3.11).

   (A) Cut Thin Slices Crosswise.—The slices may be butterflied for even wider slices.
   (B) Cut Thin Slices Lengthwise.—Cutting thin slices crosswise makes the first slices lean, but the end portion may be difficult to sell because of the fat content. Slicing lengthwise eliminates this factor because each slice will contain a portion of the end. Slices cut lengthwise can also be merchandised as a rolled meat item which some ethnic groups will request. They are generally referred to as "pork bracciole slices."

UNIT 4: Fresh Hams

Fresh hams are not readily accepted by many consumers. This is largely due to the lack of knowledge on the part of the consumer. Consumers generally regard hams purely as a smoked product. Some customers feel reluctant to purchase fresh hams because of their large size and the added time required in roasting them. Carving and serving the ham after cooking may also be a drawback. This merchandising problem may be partly attributed to retailers who are not skilled and knowledgeable in merchandising fresh hams. There are a number of merchandising techniques meat cutters can use. Each of these can meet specific consumer needs as they relate to the merchandising of fresh hams. This unit explains techniques and methods of merchandising which may apply to special needs in the merchandising of fresh hams.

Let us examine the region of the pork carcass from which the fresh ham is cut (see Fig. 4.1). When fresh hams are cut from the hog, they are generally referred to as untrimmed hams because of the attached tail, flank, and hind foot. Packers generally remove the untrimmed ham from the pork carcass side by cutting at a point approximately $2\frac{1}{4}$ to $2\frac{3}{4}$ in. from the exposed knob (posterior) of the aitch bone. This cut is very important to the packer because any slight deviation from the exact point of initial cutting will cause an irregular cut which will affect the ham, loin, or belly. This can cause a considerable loss when multiplied by the number of hogs processed each day. Packers may leave the flank on the belly when removing the flank from the ham. This will depend upon the packer's cutting procedures. The hind foot is removed by cutting through the closed joint in the hock region so as not to expose the marrow of the shank bone. This procedure may vary from packer to packer. Hind feet are rarely sold to retailers. They are generally sent to the rendering department or section to prepare them for processing into rendered pork fat. Some packers may process the feet for pickling and merchandising. The tail is removed from the ham by a ham trimmer or a skinner. These tails, if sold fresh (as many ethnic groups demand them), are packed in 30-lb boxes. Some packers will also cure them. Hams are generally marketed as skinned hams. Packers rarely merchandise regular hams (with the rind on) unless specifically requested by wholesalers or retailers. Fresh hams are skinned (rind removed) by removing $\frac{2}{3}$ of the rind from the butt portion (sirloin portion), leaving approximately $\frac{1}{3}$ of the rind around the shank end. This procedure may also vary from processor to processor. Ham skinning can be performed by machine or by hand. Care must be taken not to cut into the soft fat next to the lean surface to prevent scoring the lean meat. These skins which are removed are generally sent to the lard rendering tanks or processed into gelatin. The hams are wrapped in special packing paper, placed into corrugated boxes, and shipped to wholesalers or directly to retailers. Fresh hams are classified by weight, similar to pork loins. The most popular type of fresh ham purchased by retailers are the 14-lb to 17-lb range. There are usually four hams to a carton. The classified weight ranges of the hams are 14 lb and down, 14 to 17 lb, 17 to 20 lb, and 20 lb and up. The larger weights generally have only three hams to a carton.

Let us examine the bone structure of the fresh ham (see Fig. 4.2). The ham is composed of an aitch bone, round bone (sometimes referred to as a leg bone), the shank bone (which is also referred to as a hock and splinter bone), and the knee cap. The bones will represent approximately 12–15% of the ham. The muscle structure of the ham is similar to the leg of veal, beef, and lamb. The exception is that it does not have a full sirloin muscle. It consists of a knuckle muscle, inside round muscle, outside round muscle, heel of the round muscle, a portion of the sirloin muscle, a portion of the tenderloin muscle, and the shank muscle (refer to Fig. 4.2).

Methods of merchandising fresh hams vary. Retailers generally use basic methods such as merchandising hams whole, cut in half, fresh ham slices, or butt and shank end portions of ham. The National Livestock and Meat Board has published a small pamphlet entitled *Merchandising Legs Of Pork*. All meat cutters should have this pamphlet as a reference to assist them in cutting fresh hams. Below are some suggested methods.

CUTTING A FRESH HAM INTO A BUTT AND SHANK HALF

1. Place the ham on the movable carriage of the band saw with the exposed view of the aitch bone facing up. Cut approximately 2 in. from the knob of the aitch

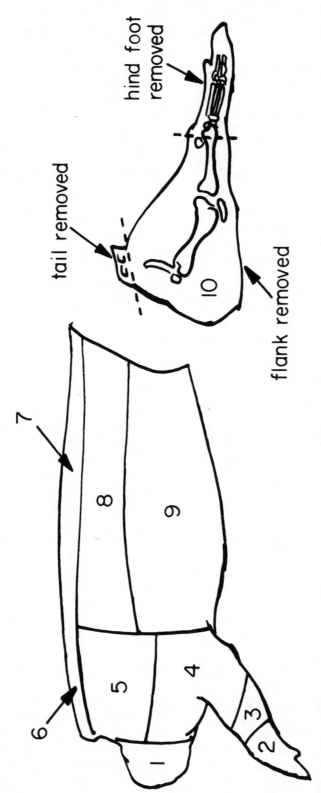

FIG. 4.1. SHOWING LOCATION OF UNTRIMMED HAM (10) ON HOG CARCASS ALONG WITH IDENTIFICATION OF OTHER CARCASS PARTS: 1—JOWL; 2—FRONT FEET; 3—KNUCKLE; 4—PICNIC SHOULDER; 5—BOSTON BUTT; 6—CLEAR PLATE; 7—BACKFAT; 8—LOIN; 9—BELLY

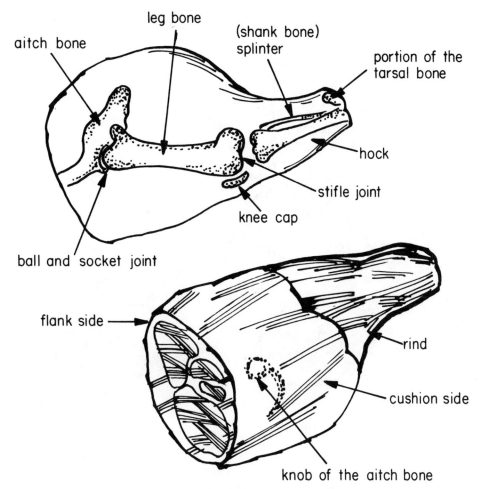

leg bone

aitch bone

(shank bone)
splinter

portion of the
tarsal bone

hock

stifle joint

knee cap

ball and socket joint

flank side

rind

cushion side

knob of the aitch bone

FIG. 4.2. BONE STRUCTURE OF A FRESH HAM

bone on a slight angle. (See Fig. 4.3.) The butt portion contains the aitch bone and half of the round bone (knob end). The shank half contains the hock and splinter bone, round bone, and the knee cap (refer back to Fig. 4.2).

Note: Some retailers may use heavy-weight hams (20 lb and up) so that they can remove some center cut slices from either half. This is not always advisable because you will be merchandising a butt end and a shank end and not ham halves. This is a form of misrepresentation. It would be advisable to use fresh hams for halves in the weight range of 14 lb and down because it is a more popular cut.

CUTTING A FRESH HAM INTO A BUTT END, SHANK END, AND CENTER SLICES

1. Remove the butt end on the band saw by cutting close to the knob of the aitch bone (see Fig. 4.3).

   Note: Cut on a slight angle so that the cushion end is larger in width than the flank end. (See Fig. 4.3.)

   Note: Some retailers remove the ball portion of the leg bone prior to merchandising the butt end. This is a matter of store merchandising practice.

2. Remove the center cut slices by cutting thicknesses that meet store merchandising practices. Do not cut to a point where you cut into the knee cap. This may create a problem in merchandising the shank end because the slice removed will have a large amount of bone (see Fig. 4.4).

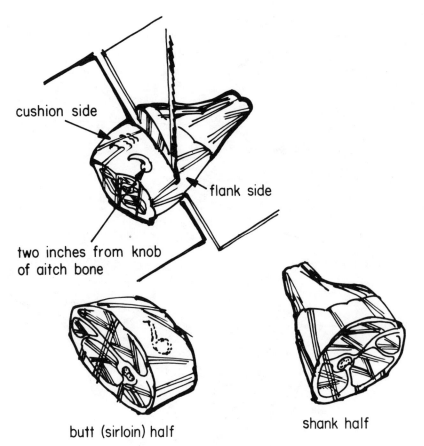

FIG. 4.3. HOW TO CUT A FRESH HAM INTO A BUTT HALF AND A SHANK
HALF

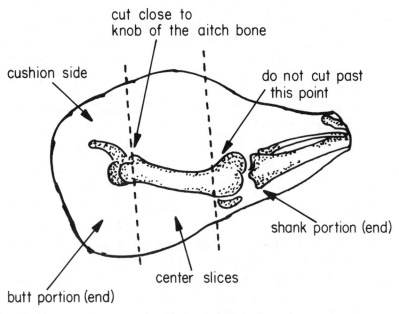

FIG. 4.4. WHERE TO CUT A FRESH HAM INTO A BUTT END, A SHANK END,
AND CENTER SLICES

Note: Meat cutters should use heavier weight hams for this type of cutting (17 lb to 20 lb and up).

Note: Flexibility is necessary when cutting center cut fresh ham slices. Some consumers prefer to broil these slices with pineapple and special sauces. These slices should be cut approximately 1 in. or more in thickness. Some customers prefer to pan fry ham slices. These slices should be cut about $\frac{1}{4}$ in. in thickness. Remove the bone dust from the slices and place them in a No. 10 boat. For 1-in. thick fresh ham steaks, place one slice to a boat. Place 2–3 slices to a boat for the thin steak slices.

BONING AND TIEING A FRESH HAM

There are various methods of boning fresh hams. Meat cutters will adjust specific methods of boning with those factors which will attract the customer as well as make the most of the characteristics related to boneless and rolled fresh hams which create sales appeal. Some of these factors relate to the size of the ham, the condition of the ham, and the processing methods employed by the establishment. Refer back to Fig. 4.2 to familiarize yourself with the bone structure of the fresh ham.

Chain stores and supermarkets rarely bone and tie fresh hams, either in a whole form or in a cut form, because of the added costs of time and labor. Restaurants and institutions most always purchase fresh hams which are boned and rolled. It is more efficient and effective to cook and serve. This is also true of many consumers who purchase fresh hams in retail stores. It is necessary for meat cutters to have the skill and knowledge applicable to boning and tieing fresh hams. This will increase the tonnage of pork sales. The following are suggested methods.

Boning and Tieing Method No. 1

1. Remove the entire shank at the stifle joint. (See Fig. 4.5.)

   Note: Locate the stifle joint by feeling for the end of the knee cap. There may be a slight indentation at this point.

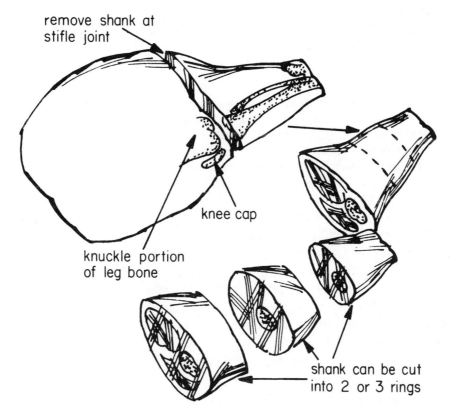

remove shank at
stifle joint

knee cap

knuckle portion
of leg bone

shank can be cut
into 2 or 3 rings

FIG. 4.5. SHANK OF HAM CAN BE REMOVED AND CUT INTO RINGS

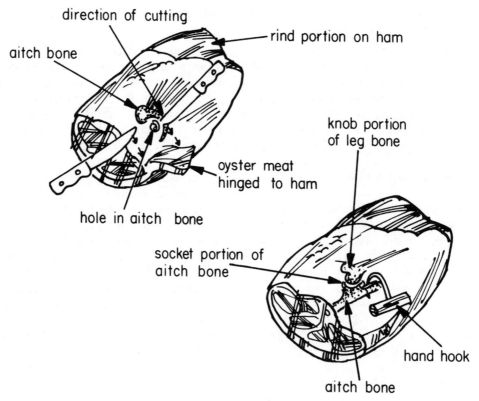

FIG. 4.6. PROCEDURE FOR REMOVING AITCH BONE FROM A HAM

Note: The shank may be merchandised or cut into 2 or 3 rings and labeled "fresh ham hocks." By first removing the entire shank, boning of the fresh ham becomes a simpler operation.

2. Loosen and lay back the oyster meat which lies in the cavity of the aitch bone (see Fig. 4.6).

Note: Some meat cutters may leave the oyster meat attached to the ham and return to the cavity before tieing the ham. It is advisable to remove the oyster meat and use it as trimmings for ground pork or mix it with lean trimmings to make pork cubed steaks. There are two obvious reasons for this procedure: (1) The oyster meat may fall out during roasting or baking. (2) The oyster meat may fall out or separate from the cooked slice when the ham is cut and served.

3. Remove the aitch bone by following the contour of the bone and cutting the cord through the ball and socket joint.

Caution: Do not cut upward. Always keep the tip of the knife against the bone. Use a small hand hook or your free hand in order to place your fingers through the hole of the aitch bone to assist you in removing the aitch bone (see Fig. 4.6).

4. Using the tip of your boning knife, loosen all the meat from the knob portion of the leg bone (see Fig. 4.7).

Caution: Keep the tip of the knife against the bone to prevent making a large opening.

Note: This method is known as tunneling. Some meat cutters will scrape with the heel of the knife to catch the seam after freeing the knob end of the leg bone.

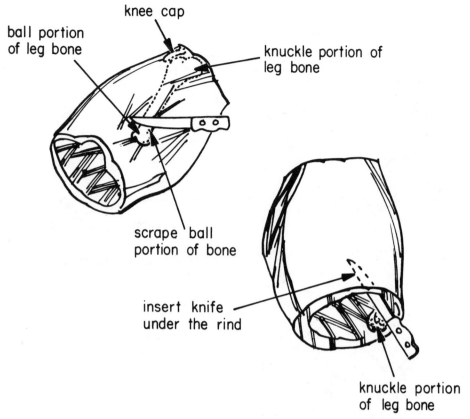

ball portion
of leg bone

knee cap

knuckle portion of
leg bone

scrape ball
portion of bone

insert knife
under the rind

knuckle portion
of leg bone

FIG. 4.7. PROCEDURE FOR REMOVING LEG BONE FROM A HAM

5. To free the meat from the knuckle portion of the leg bone, follow the same procedure as in step No. 4 above.

   Note: Twist the leg bone free from the ham. The bone can then be removed
   from either end. It is advisable to catch the seam on both sides of the leg
   bone before twisting the leg bone free from the ham. *Make sure that the
   knee cap is removed from the ham.* Some meat cutters may forget this
   bone and proceed to tie the fresh ham. If this bone is left as a regular
   practice, restaurant and institutional buyers may discontinue purchase because of the problems arising when slicing and serving the cooked ham.
   This also applies to the retail consumer who slices cooked meats by hand.

6. Place a double guide string around the length of the ham. (Strings should be
   placed around both the center and the sides of the ham.) (See Fig. 4.8A.)

   Note: Some meat cutters may use only one guide string around the center of the
   ham. Some may not use any guide strings at all. This is not recommended
   practice. Guide strings will keep the fresh ham in a rectangular shape. It
   will also prevent bulging at specific portions of the ham because of the
   natural muscle structure of the ham.

7. Place the first cross string approximately in the center of the ham. (See Fig.
   4.8B.)

   Note: Because of the natural structure of the ham, the top sirloin muscle may
   tend to slip from the position of the cord. Try to catch the center of the
   top sirloin muscle to prevent it from slipping. This may cause the first
   cross string to be off center. However, this may be corrected after the
   entire ham is rolled and tied (see Fig. 4.8C).

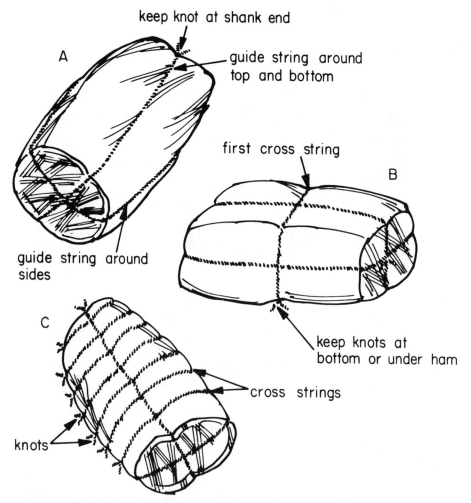

FIG. 4.8. TO TIE A BONELESS FRESH HAM: (A) USE GUIDE STRING AROUND SIDES AND
AROUND TOP AND BOTTOM; (B) PUT FIRST CROSS STRING AT CENTER; (C) THEN FINISH
WITH CROSS STRINGS AS SHOWN

8. Continue to place cross strings approximately 1 in. apart from the center string
   alternating from one side to the other. This will prevent bulges in the finished
   product. (See Fig. 4.8C.)

Boning and Tieing Method No. 2

To bone and tie a fresh ham with the shank meat portion attached to the ham,
eliminate step No. 1 in the boning method No. 1 for boning a fresh ham (above)
then follow steps No. 2 and No. 3 and proceed as follows:

1. Locate the knee cap at the stifle joint. Insert a thin boning knife through the
   rind, thereby cutting the cord between the leg bone and shank bone. (See
   Fig. 4.9.)

   Note: Avoid making a large hole in the rind at the stifle joint.

2. Insert the boning knife (at the hock end) under the rind between the rind and the
   shank meat. Circle the entire shank. This will loosen the entire shank from the
   rind. (See Fig. 4.10.)

3. Remove the entire shank (bone and meat) from the rind. Bone out the splinter
   bone and the hock bone.

   Note: Some meat cutters will use a steel to assist them in removing the shank
           (see Fig. 4.11).

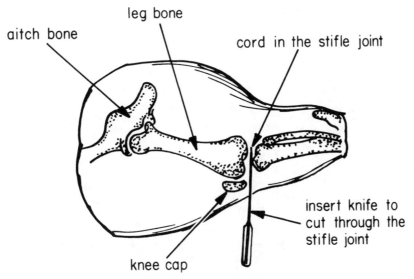

FIG. 4.9. CUT THE CORD THROUGH THE STIFLE JOINT

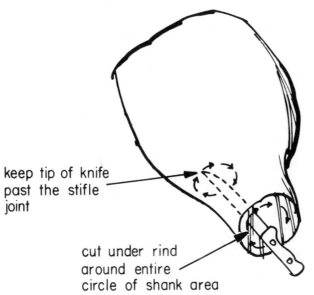

FIG. 4.10. LOOSEN SHANK AREA BY INSERTING KNIFE UNDER RIND

4. Replace the boneless shank meat in the cavity of the shank.
5. Proceed as in step No. 4 in method No. 5 (boning a fresh ham) to remove the leg bone from the ham.

   Note: The bone must be removed from the butt end of the ham and not the shank end.

   Prior to the actual tieing of the boneless fresh ham, stitch the end of the fresh ham (hock end) with a needle and twine (this requires about 1–2 stitches) to prevent the shank meat from bulging out of the shank cavity. You may follow the same procedure as that followed in method No. 1 when tieing the fresh ham with the shank meat, or you may use the following method:

6. Place a cross string around the center of the fresh ham and secure the knot.

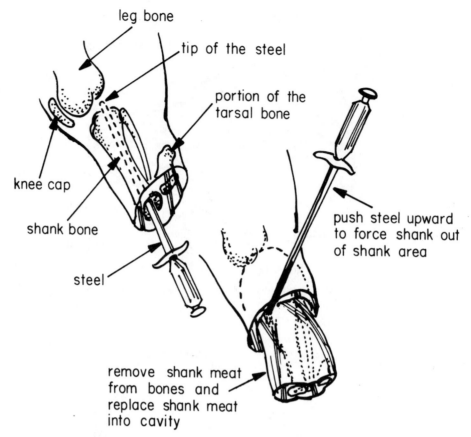

FIG. 4.11. WEDGE SHANK MEAT (WITH BONE IN) OUT OF HAM USING STEEL; THEN BONE SHANK MEAT AND REPLACE IN CAVITY

Note: Leave enough string on one end that will be approximately long enough to circle the fresh ham 8 to 10 times, depending upon the size of the ham. (See Fig. 4.12.)

7. Place evenly-placed cross strings around half of the ham by weaving the cross strings as shown in Fig. 4.12.

Note: Use your free hand to assist you in shaping the fresh ham.

8. Turn the ham upside down (fat surface facing up) and interlace a loop around each cross string (see Fig. 4.13).

9. Repeat tieing cross strings on the other half of the ham as shown in Fig. 4.13. Then turn the ham right side up (lean surface facing up) and interlace a loop around each cross string on the other side of the ham. Secure the ends with a knot in the center of the ham and remove excess twine. (See Fig. 4.14.)

CUTTING A FRESH HAM INTO THREE BONELESS PORK ROASTS

Retail meat cutters should be sufficiently skilled and knowledgeable regarding hams and other pork cuts in order to meet most competitive situations related to the processing and merchandising of heavy fresh hams. The weight range of fresh hams ordinarily used for processing into 3 or 4 small roasts would be either in the 17–20 lb range or in the 20 lb and up range. In processing, it is advisable to remove the shank portion of the fresh ham at the stifle joint before proceeding to bone and cut the remaining portion of the fresh ham into retail cuts. It is important to remember that meat cutters do not usually trim boneless cuts from the fresh ham. Fresh hams are generally lean and the little fat remaining on the ham will make for a juicier and more flavorful roast. Trimming will cause an increase in the retail selling price and may even be a cause for placing the meat retailer out of competition with other meat retailers. The following are suggested methods for cutting a fresh ham into pork roasts.

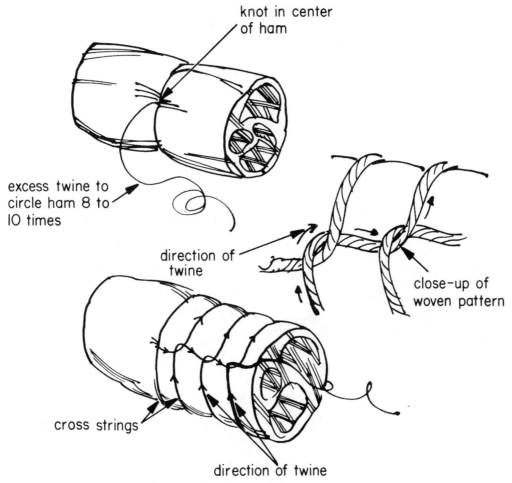

knot in center of ham

excess twine to circle ham 8 to 10 times

direction of twine

close-up of woven pattern

cross strings

direction of twine

FIG. 4.12. HOW TO WEAVE AND SECURE CROSS STRINGS ON A BONELESS HAM WITH INSIDE SURFACE FACING UP

Boning Heavy Fresh Hams

1. Remove the shank portion of the ham at the stifle joint. Refer back to Fig. 4.5 for merchandising the shank. If there is little consumer demand for fresh ham hocks, it is advisable to bone and skin the shank. The meat processed from the shank can be cubed or ground and then merchandised as a meat loaf item or some other meat item on the menu.

2. Remove the aitch bone (refer back to Fig. 4.6).

3. Cut through the lean meat between the inside muscle and the sirloin tip muscle, keeping the tip of the knife against the side of the leg bone. (See Fig. 4.15A.)

    Caution: Do not cut too deep. You may score the silver seam on the outside muscle. This may then require extra trimming.

4. Continue to follow the contour of the underside of the leg bone to locate the seam between the sirloin tip muscle and the outside muscle. (See Fig. 4.15B.)

    Note: This seam is similar to that of beef when pulling a knuckle face from the beef primal round. The muscle structure is the same except that they are much smaller in size.

5. Continue to follow the contour of the leg bone by keeping the tip of the boning knife against the bone. The bone can be removed from either end; the ball end or the knuckle end. (See Fig. 4.15C.)

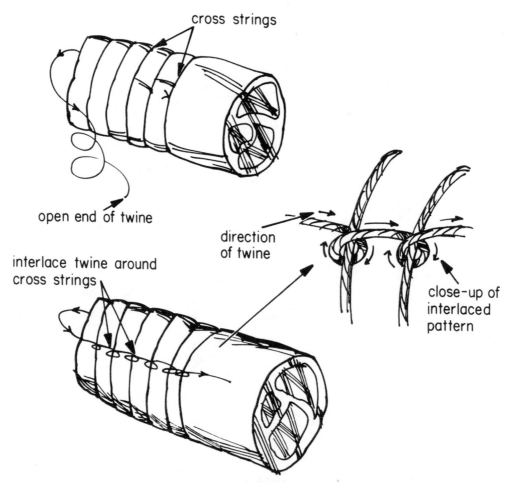

FIG. 4.13. HOW TO INTERLACE CROSS STRINGS ON BONELESS HAM WITH OUTSIDE SURFACE FACING UP

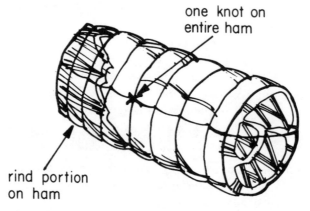

FIG. 4.14. THIS IS THE FINISHED TIED BONELESS HAM USING BOTH THE WEAVING METHOD AND THE INTERLACING METHOD OF TIEING

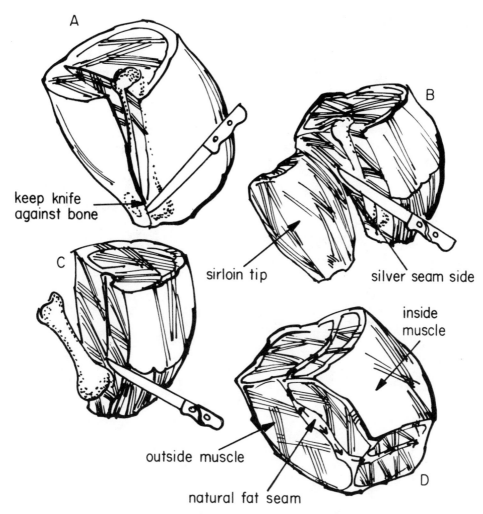

keep knife
against bone

sirloin tip   silver seam side

inside
muscle

outside muscle

natural fat seam

FIG. 4.15. TO SEPARATE SHANKLESS HAM INTO THREE MUSCLES: (A) START CUTTING AT
THE KNOB END; (B) CUT UNDERSIDE OF BONE FROM SEAM; (C) REMOVE LEG BONE; AND
(D) SEPARATE MUSCLES

6. To remove the inside muscle from the outside muscle, follow the natural fat seam
   between the two muscles at the point where the leg bone was removed. (See Fig.
   4.15D.)

   Note: Keep the portion of the heel muscle and the sirloin muscle attached to the
   outside muscle.

Merchandising the Boneless Muscles as Roasts

Notes On Tieing Boneless Roasts

Guide strings should be tied loosely rather than very taut. This will allow for the
even distribution of the muscle meat when forming the roast. Meat establishments
are often equipped with automatic twine tieing machines. This machine is an efficient processing adjunct for increasing productivity in the rolling and tieing of roasts.
Some meat establishments may be equipped with a hand operated or automatic "Jet
Net Machine." This machine places an elastic, tubular netting on the roast as it is
pushed through a flexible cylinder applicator or shaper. This netting makes for an
attractive cut of meat. However, after the roast is cooked, the netting often tends to
adhere to the roast.

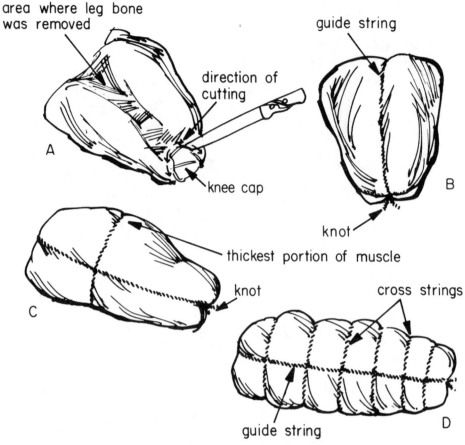

FIG. 4.16. TO TIE A SIRLOIN TIP MUSCLE FROM A FRESH HAM: (A) TRIM OUT KNEE CAP; (B) PLACE GUIDE STRING AROUND LENGTH AND SIDES OF MUSCLE; (C) KEEP KNOTS AT BOTTOM AND END; (D) FINISH WITH CROSS STRINGS AS SHOWN

The Sirloin Tip Muscle (Top Sirloin) (Knuckle Face)

It is not advisable to remove any part of the outside layer of fat located at the natural seam. Leave the sirloin tip as it is. It is also not advisable to use this muscle to make pork cutlets or cube steaks. The seam between the three muscles within the sirloin tip thickens toward the knee cap area and may become tough. It is advisable to merchandise this muscle in its entirety for roasting.

1. Remove the knee cap. (See Fig. 4.16A.)
2. Place one or two guide strings lengthwise on the sirloin tip muscle. (See Fig. 4.16B.)
3. Place the first cross string at the thickest portion of the muscle. (See Fig. 4.16C.)
4. Tie evenly-spaced cross strings, approximately 1 or 2 finger thicknesses apart, starting at the thickest portion of the muscle. (See Fig. 4.16D.)

The Inside Muscle (Top)

The only trimming necessary on the inside muscle may require the removal of the thin membrane or discolored meat from the exposed surface above the point where the aitch bone was removed (see Fig. 4.17A). The inside muscle may be merchandised whole as a roast, or it can be sliced. The following are suggested methods for processing.

Follow the same procedure employed when tieing a sirloin tip muscle. Omit step No. 1 and use only 1 guide string lengthwise instead of 2. Some meat cutters may omit all the guide strings and proceed to tie only cross strings on the roast. This is a matter of store merchandising practice. (See Fig. 4.17B.)

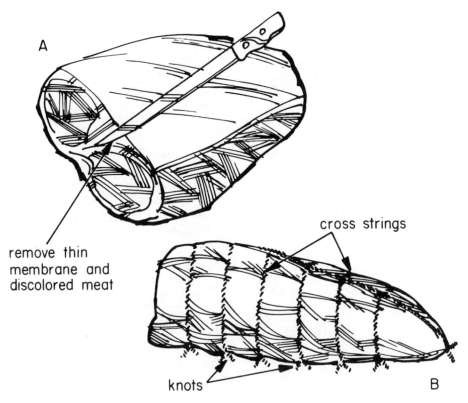

FIG. 4.17. TOP VIEW (A) OF INSIDE MUSCLE BEFORE TIEING AND (B) SIDE VIEW OF TIED
INSIDE MUSCLE

Follow the steps below for slicing the inside muscle.

1. Remove the first slice, starting at the point where the aitch bone was removed. Cut at a slight angle. This will make for a wider slice of meat because of the slight angle. A straight cut will result in a smaller slice or cut.

   Note: The first slice may be merchandised for a cube steak. This will eliminate the necessity for further trimming of the slice that has been removed. Some meat cutters may cube or grind the first slice for a meat loaf or other chopped meat item.

2. Continue to cut thin slices at an angle approximately ⅛- to ¼-in. thick. Merchandise these slices for pork cutlets (see Fig. 4.18).

   Note: These pork slices may also be cut ½- to ¾-in. thick and merchandised as boneless fresh ham steaks. This is also a matter of store policy and merchandising practices. Cutlets generally retail at a higher selling price than steaks.

3. It is advisable to separate and remove the thin layer of meat on top of the inside muscle after slicing through approximately half of the muscle (see Fig. 4.19).

   Note: If this thin layer of meat is to be used for pork cube steak, no further trimming is necessary. If it is to be used for cutlets, it should be trimmed of all excess fat. (See Fig. 4.19.) The very end portion of the inside muscle may be butterflied to even out the thickness of the meat. It will also widen the slice of the remaining cut.

Outside Muscle (Bottom)

Depending upon merchandising need and consumer preference, the outside muscle can be used for slicing purposes or sold whole as a roast. If sold whole, no further trimming is necessary. If sliced, the sirloin portion and the heel portion

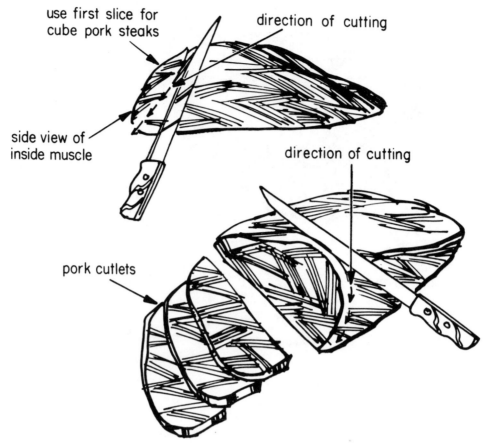

FIG. 4.18. INSIDE MUSCLE ALSO MAY BE SLICED FOR CUTLETS AS SHOWN

must be removed from the outside muscle before slicing. It is advisable not to trim the outside muscle because of high labor costs. Time is also an important factor in merchandising. The following is an efficient method for tieing the outside muscle.

1. Place the outisde muscle on the bench with the outside surface facing the bench and the inside surface facing up (see Step No. 1, Fig. 4.20).
2. Place a stitch with the roast beef tier (needle) securing the portion of the sirloin muscle on the roast (see Fig. 4.20, Step No. 2).
3. Place another stitch at the opposite end securing the heel portion of the roast (see Fig. 4.20, Step No. 3).
4. Place 2 or 3 stitches evenly spaced along the length of the roast. This will form the roast into a cylindrical shape.
5. Place a guide string lengthwise on the roast (see Fig. 4.20, Step No. 4).
6. Place evenly-spaced cross strings around the roast. Be sure to place the knots at the bottom of the roast.

   Note: As a result of boning heavy fresh hams as described above it is now possible for the small family to purchase a particular portion of the ham for various meal requirements. For example, an excellent portion used for stuffing is the outside muscle because it is flat in shape. Meat cutters may or may not remove that portion of the sirloin and heel attached to the outside muscle before making a pocket within the flesh of the muscle. If the outside muscle is to be used as a stuffed meat item, it is advisable to remove that portion of the sirloin and heel.

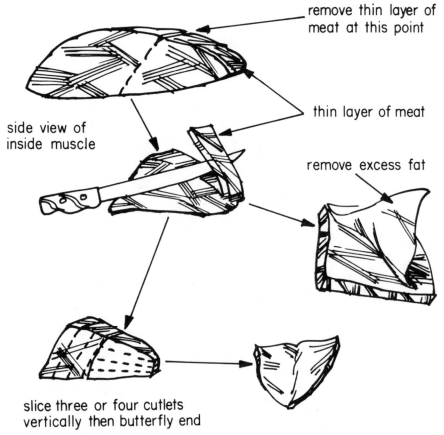

remove thin layer of
meat at this point

thin layer of meat

side view of
inside muscle

remove excess fat

slice three or four cutlets
vertically then butterfly end

FIG. 4.19. MERCHANDISING END PORTION OF THE INSIDE MUSCLE BY MAKING
CUTLETS AND BUTTERFLIED STEAKS

SMOKING AND CURING HAMS AND OTHER PORK PRODUCTS

Smoking

The science of smoking meats is increasing rapidly in the number of techniques and procedures. There are various methods packers may use to smoke meats. Basically, smoking is a process whereby the product is exposed to smoke within a smokehouse (metal chamber) with controlled temperatures and smoke concentration for a specific length of time. The actual process is scientifically controlled and will vary in accordance with the packer's processing practices.

Packers have developed techniques and processes in the meat industry to an advanced state. This is particularly so with regard to the processing of hams. Smoked hams and related pork products are now generally processed and fabricated into many different types of retail cuts. The packaging of these cuts has also reached an advanced state. Cry-O-Vac and similar packaging equipment, wrap and package cuts with shape and contour of the meat cut that is packaged. This makes for a more attractive display and more efficient merchandising.

Labeling of the product is usually all that is required of the merchandiser.

In many instances, it would be advantageous for meat retailers to process their own smoked meat cuts by following the same procedures for smoked hams as for fresh ham cuts. Many chain stores and supermarkets feel that preprocessing and prepackaging are a savings because of the high labor costs and cost of packaging materials. However, many retailers are of the opinion that it is advantageous for them to cut their own smoked products. Many meat cutters are not familiar with the procedures of curing and smoking meats. Therefore, it is important that a basic knowledge of curing and smoking be a part of the meat cutter's experience to assist him in the merchandising of these products.

Curing

Through the practical and scientific advancement of meat technology and the techniques of curing, retailers no longer cure their own meat products. They are purchased from the packer or wholesaler in a cured, smoked, bone-in or boneless state, and attractively packaged. The retailer merely

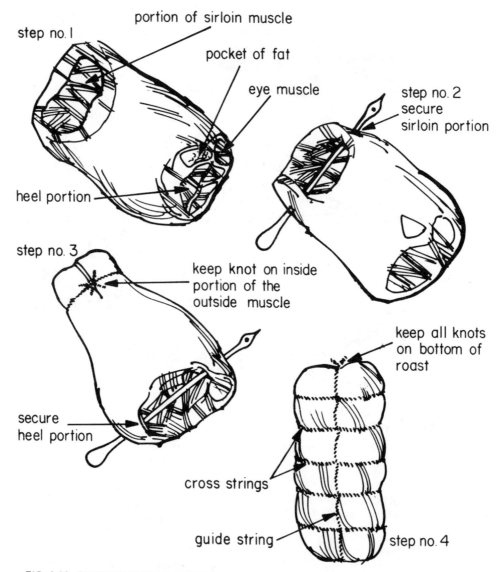

FIG. 4.20. SHOWING THE FOUR STEPS IN TIEING THE OUTSIDE MUSCLE INTO A ROAST

places an identifying label and merchandising tag on the product.

The prime reason for curing meats is to preserve the meats as long as possible. At present, the additional purposes for curing include improvement of palatability, color, flavor, tenderness, and to increase the merchandising potential through availability of a greater variety of cuts. Thus, through modern technological advances and the science of meat preservation, cured meats have increased the product variety and offer a greater menu selection to the consumer.

Basically, there are five methods of curing meats. They are briefly explained below.

1. The Dry Curing Method

In dry curing, the product is rubbed with a salt mixture[1] and the meat is refrigerated until the salt

penetrates to the center of the product. (The size and type of cut will determine the amount of time required for thorough curing.) During this refrigeration period, the surface of the product is re-rubbed periodically and generally placed in vats or other holding equipment until cured. This process is not actually a dry cure. When the vats are filled, the weight and pressure of the meats being cured causes natural meat juices to be extracted from the meat. This forms a natural pickling solution which envelops the meat and acts as a brine. In the dry curing process, some packers will add ascorbates or phosphates during the rubbing process. Some packers will brine-inject the product and then

[1] A very limited number of products are cured with salt alone. However, salt is the main component in a dry cure mixture which will generally be combined with nitrite and/or nitrate in very small quantity for the pink color that will then develop.

apply a dry rub or salt. This practice reduces curing time. Specific curing techniques used by packers are a matter of the packer's own production policy.

2. The Brine Soaking Method

The brine soaking method requires the product to be placed in a solution (called "pickle") composed of water and salt usually with chemical additives. In due time, depending upon the size of the cut, the brine penetrates through the entire product. Some packers use brine soaking for curing small items. The strength or concentration of the brine will depend upon the packer's curing procedures. Many packers reuse the same brine, but this has been found to be poor practice. The used brine often becomes contaminated with bacteria from the meat juices.

3. The Brine Injection Method

Brine injection, commonly referred to as pumping, is the forceable injection of brine into the meat muscle. This method shortens the curing time of the product being cured. Actually, there are three different methods of brine injection. One is called stitch or spray pumping. This type of brine injection is accomplished with a needle that has a number of holes along the shank. The needle is inserted into the muscle and the brine forced into the product in order to cure the product. This curing action works from the inside to the outside of the product. After the product has been pumped, it is then placed into vats which are called holding vats where the brine finishes the cure.

4. The Artery Pumping Method

The artery pumping method is another form of brine injection. In this method, the brine is injected into the femoral artery (butt end of the ham below the aitch bone area) with a needle attached to a pressure hose containing the brine. The brine flows through the arterial system and to the capillary blood vessels of the product being cured. It has been found that this procedure has certain disadvantages. This is due to the fact that 25–50% of the hams cured in this manner have damaged arteries, or have arteries which have dried up before being pumped.

5. The Machine Pumping Method

Machine pumping is considered to be one of the best and most improved method of pumping. This is a machine with a moving belt to carry the product to an overhead injection panel containing multiple needles with holes in the shank of the needles to inject the brine solution into the product. Cure is distributed thoroughly and at a much faster rate. For example, hams that are machine pumped can go directly to the smoke house without first being placed in holding brine vats. This type of pumping is the most advanced and accepted type in the meat industry.

UNIT 5: Merchandising Miscellaneous Pork Products

The merchandising of miscellaneous pork products may require merchandising supervisors and managers to be more aggressive in their merchandising practices. The planned display of these products in the meat case may encourage a greater volume of sales and profits for the store or meat department of supermarkets. Many of these specialty pork products have an unusually fine flavor and they are high in nutritive value. For example, the offal products—especially the internal organs—are very rich in vitamin mineral content. Some specialty items in particular are purchased by various ethnic group consumers who rely solely on chain stores and supermarkets to carry these specialty pork products.

Meat men should be alert to the proper methods of displaying and merchandising specialty pork items. For example, mix and match items in the case such as liver and bacon, pork feet and cabbage, hocks and sauerkraut, neck bones and garden vegetables make a good display. Care should be observed that other mix items placed in the same display case are packaged properly to prevent absorption of foreign odors and to maintain cleanliness of all products on display. Transfer of bacteria from one food product to another will also create losses due to spoilage.

In many instances, a consumer will shop in a chain store or supermarket because of the large assortment of items available for purchase. The consumer may not have any definite purchases in mind, but prefers to pick, choose, consider, mix, and match before making a final selection. Very often, the consumer is looking for menu and serving ideas from the large selection on display. A consumer will often purchase meat items on impulse because of the attractiveness of the display. Consumers appreciate special displays because they may be reminded of meat items they need and have forgotten or overlooked. This also provides the consumer with an opportunity to widen the scope and variety of meat dishes to be cooked and served. As for the meat men, it is important to remember that pigs' feet, pigs' tails, or kidneys cannot be readily merchandised unless they are on display in the meat case. A consumer is often swayed by the feel and appeal of the packaged items to make a purchase. If recipes for menu items that require the use of pork specialties are available from reliable home economics sources, or even neighborhood specialty sources, these should be distributed to encourage the sale of pork specialties. Versatility in merchandising is necessary and various approaches should be tried.

Pork Hocks

Pork hocks are that part of the front shank above the knuckle joint (carpal joint) where the foot is cut off. Some retailers refer to these shanks as pigs' knuckles. The type of hock will vary from packer to packer depending upon their methods of merchandising and processing. (Refer back to Fig. 3.2 in Unit 3.) Retailers purchase hocks (fresh, smoked, or frozen) in cartons of varying weights. The most popular size is approximately 25 lb per carton. Hocks can be merchandised whole, paired, or cut up into 2 or 3 portions (see Fig. 5.1).

Pork Feet

Generally, the bulk of the pork feet sold in retail stores comes from the fore feet. They are called front feet and consumers refer to them as pigs' feet. The hind feet from the carcass are usually sent to the tank to be rendered into grease. Retailers can purchase short-cut or long-cut front feet. Differences are shown in Fig. 5.2. When merchandising front feet, it is important to remember that consumers prefer that they be split in half lengthwise. Caution must be observed when using the band saw to split pigs' feet. More accidents occur on the band saw while splitting pigs' feet than any other item because meat men are often lax and neglect using the safety plate. The packaging of pigs' feet will vary from store to store depending upon consumer requests. (See Fig. 5.2.)

Pork Tails

Generally, tails are sold to the consumer and rarely used in the manufacture of any kind of sausage or lard. They are quite bony and are generally cooked with sauerkraut, cabbage, green leafy vegetables, dried beans, peas, root vegetables, or

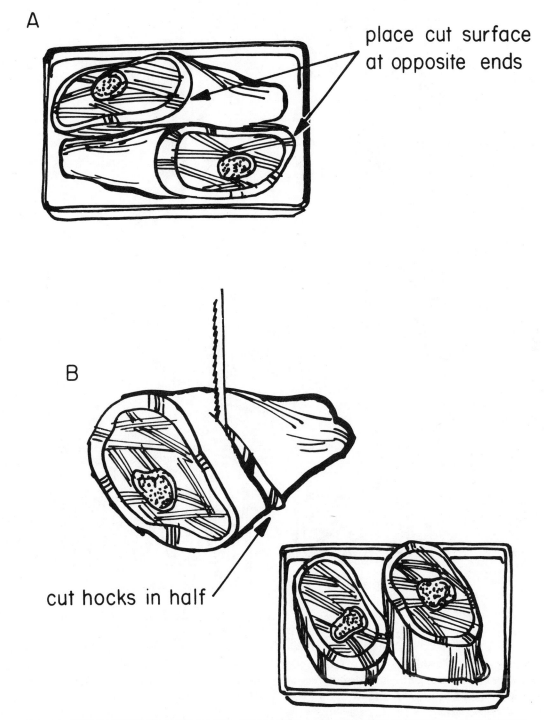

place cut surface at opposite ends

cut hocks in half

FIG. 5.1. MERCHANDISING PORK HOCKS: (A) PLACE A PAIR OF HOCKS IN BOAT, OR (B) CUT HOCK RINGS AND PACKAGE 2 OR 3 TOGETHER

lentils. They are considered quite a delicacy within various ethnic groups. Retailers purchase tails in 25- or 30-lb boxes in a frozen state. Merchandise the tails by cutting them in half and packaging them in various weights for consumer selection (see Fig. 5.3).

Hogs' Heads

Hogs' heads are rarely merchandised in retail stores, although they can be ordered from the packer. Packers generally process the head by separating it into the tongue, cheek meat, brains,

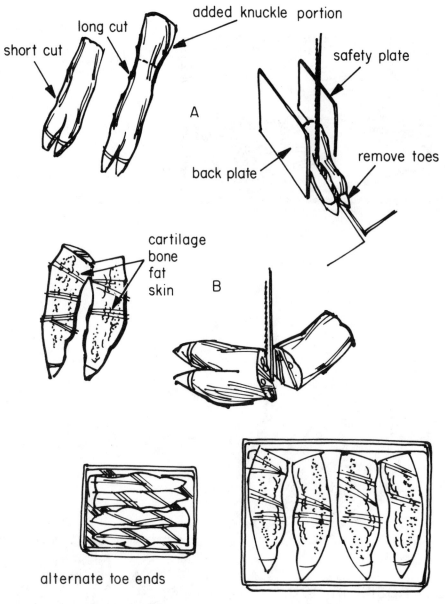

FIG. 5.2. MERCHANDISING FRONT FEET: SPLIT LENGTHWISE (A) OR CROSSWISE (B)
AND PACKAGE AS SHOWN

ears, snouts, and lips. The tongues are trimmed and used for pickled tongue or as a sausage meat. The snout and ears are removed and sold in the same manner as pigs' tails. Jowl fat and lips are removed, trimmed, and generally frozen and are sold to sausage manufacturers. Temple meat is removed from the head and usually sold in frozen containers. They are sold to sausage manufacturers or made into pork cutlets. Jowl trimmings from the lower jaw are generally sold to sausage manufacturers.

Jowls

Jowls are rarely found in retail stores. They are generally processed into jowl bacon squares by the packers. Fresh jowls are usually purchased by sausage manufacturers because they consist mainly of fat and are commonly referred to as cheek meat.

Fat Backs

Fat backs are mostly sent to the salt and curing rooms to be processed into salted fat backs. Rarely do packers sell fresh fat back although there are some ethnic groups who prefer the fresh type to the salted variety. They are generally packed in cartons of various weights for purchase by retailers. Retailers usually merchandise fat back in portions rather than slicing them. This is a matter of individual store policy and practice.

Note: Fresh fat backs can be sliced to cover

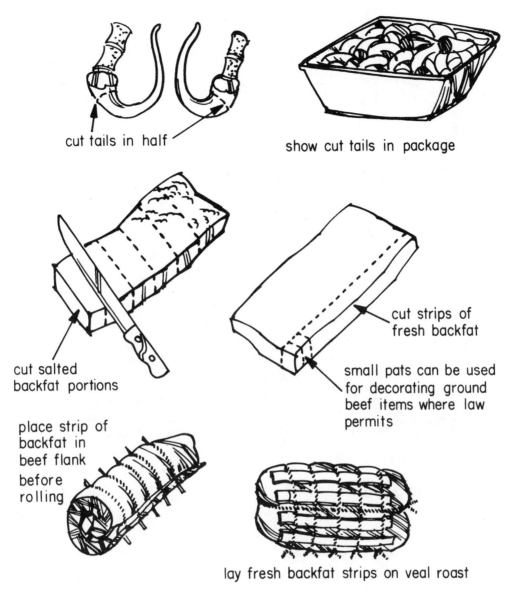

cut tails in half

show cut tails in package

cut salted backfat portions

cut strips of fresh backfat

small pats can be used for decorating ground beef items where law permits

place strip of backfat in beef flank before rolling

lay fresh backfat strips on veal roast

FIG. 5.3. MERCHANDISING TAILS AND BACKFAT

lean beef and veal roasts where local laws permit this type of merchandising. Some restaurants and hotels may prefer fat covering their lean roasts. This is a matter of choice. (See Fig. 5.3.)

Pork Livers

A large percentage of livers are used by sausage manufacturers in making various liver items such as liver sausage, liver loaf, and Braunschweiger, etc. Retailers who merchandise pork livers purchase them in 10-lb pails with 4 to 6 pails to a carton, depending upon the packers' methods of merchandising. Retailers should keep the livers in a chilled state when slicing. They can then be frozen and displayed either in the fresh meat or frozen meat open display case. (See Fig. 5.4.)

Pork Kidneys

Retailers purchase kidneys in 10-lb pails or 25-lb boxes in a frozen state. No cutting is required. Meat cutters simply place them in waxed paper containers or trays, in varying weights for consumer selection.

Pork Hearts

The heart is removed from the pluck and cut open and trimmed of all blood clots. It is then placed in ice water. Packers sell them in fresh or frozen state to the retailers. Most of the hearts are sold to sausage manufacturers. Hearts are rich in nutrients and provide for a lean, delicious piece of meat. The pork heart is as valuable as any other

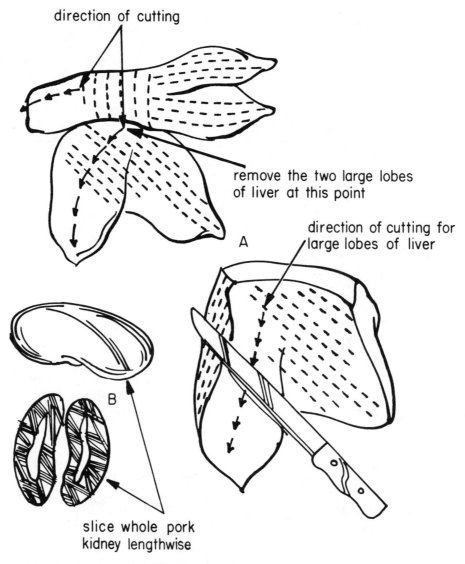

FIG. 5.4. MERCHANDISING PORK KIDNEY AND LIVER: (A) SEPARATE LIVER LOBES AND SLICE; (B) SLICE KIDNEYS LENGTHWISE

NOTE: Slice pork liver in a partially frozen state; it will slice more evenly. Then package following store merchandising practice and place packaged slices in freezer display case.

cut of meat and gives the consumer as much, and possibly more, nutritive value. Education of the consumer and improved merchandising practices will enhance the merchandising value of the heart.

Pork Brains

Retailers purchase pork brains in a frozen state from the wholesaler or packer in 5- or 10-lb pails. No cutting is necessary. They are placed in containers of varying sizes for merchandising.

Snouts

Retailers purchase snouts in a frozen state from the wholesaler or the packer in 30-lb boxes. They are a portion of the head and are composed largely of skin. They produce quite a quantity of gelatin when cooked and are used for this purpose where this type of gelatin effect is desired. Consumers of specific ethnic groups buy them to be cooked with green vegetables, dried peas, etc. They are also used for festive occasions in the preparation of homemade head cheese and various jellied meat items.

Chitterlings

Packers freeze chitterlings in 2-, 5- and 10-lb pails. No further cutting is necessary except for display in the open display case. Chitterlings are the hog's middle portion of the intestine. They are sometimes referred to as the "black gut," which is between the small intestines and the hog bung. They are approximately 3 ft long and are mostly sold to retailers in the south. They are considered quite a delicacy by members of specific ethnic groups. They are also purchased by sausage manufacturers for the casing of certain sausage items. They are also used as an ingredient in certain classes of sausage items.

Neck Bones

Neck bones are packed in 25- or 30-lb boxes. They can be purchased fresh, frozen, or smoked. They contain a high percentage of bone but the

meat remaining on the bone makes them very tasty. In cooking, quite a bit of the flavor is cooked out of the bony section which accounts for their being so unusually flavorsome. Many ethnic groups use them for seasoning sauces and flavoring various green vegetables. Neck bones may be cut into 3 to 5 pieces and placed into boats of varying sizes for customer selection (see Fig. 5.5).

Bellies

Only a small amount of bellies is sold directly to retailers in either fresh or frozen form. They are generally processed into bacon by the packer. If fresh bellies are sold to retailers, they are generally referred to as rib bellies because they have the

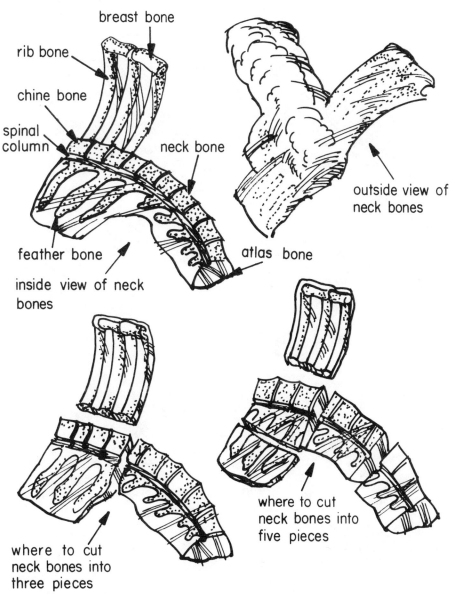

FIG. 5.5. MERCHANDISING NECK BONES

spareribs attached to the belly. Some of the smaller stores that feature only pork products and manufacture their own sausage will handle this type of cut. The fat from the belly portion will make a sweeter and finer textured type of sausage product (fresh) which various ethnic groups prefer. Refer back to Fig. 3.1 in Unit 3 to locate the area of the belly on the hog carcass.

Spareribs

With ever-increasing demand for spareribs, retailers are using varying, and often fanciful, names for different types of ribs removed from the hog carcass. Basically, there are many types of ribs which the retailer can merchandise as spareribs with the proper label on the package. Retailers usually purchase what is normally called the regular sparerib. Packers refer to them as full sheet spareribs removed from the belly portion of the carcass. (Refer back to Fig. 2.1 of Unit 2.) The full sheet of ribs consists of approximately 13 rib bones, the breast bone, and rib bone cartilages. Another type of rib is called the loin back rib which generally consists of meat between the rib bones from the pork loin which was boned in the processing of Canadian style bacon. Loin back ribs are mainly purchased by the hotel, restaurant, and institutional trades. The reason retailers do not purchase loin back ribs is that they cost much more than the

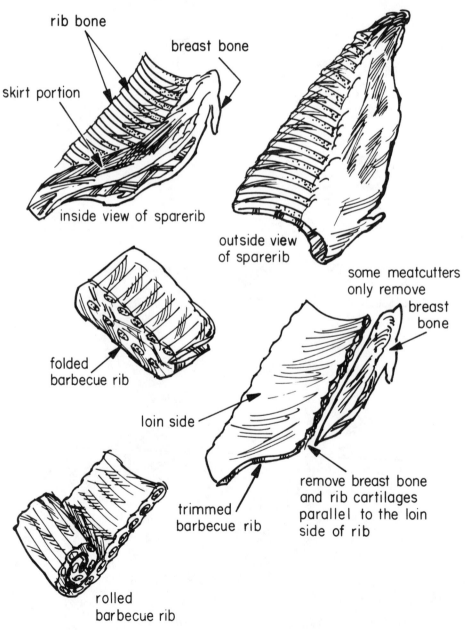

FIG. 5.6. MERCHANDISING BARBECUE SPARERIBS

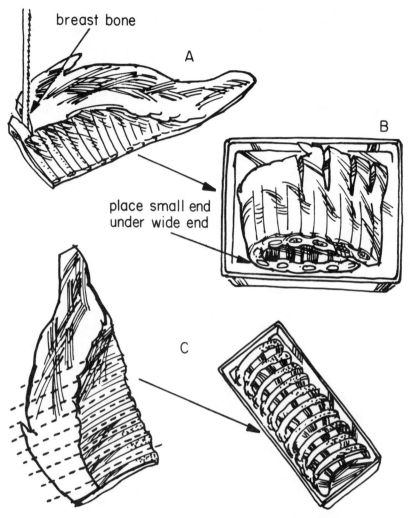

FIG. 5.7. MERCHANDISING REGULAR SPARERIBS: (A) CUT BREAST BONE BETWEEN RIB BONES AND (B) PACKAGE FULL SHEET OF RIBS; OR, (C) SLICE BETWEEN RIB BONES AND PACKAGE WITH CUT SIDE OF RIB UP AS SHOWN

regular ribs. Another type of rib is called the barbecue rib. These ribs can be prepared by meat cutters (see Fig. 5.6). Barbecue ribs are the same as regular type spareribs with the brisket bone portion removed. Spareribs essentially are fresh pork products and are sold in retail markets especially in the summer season because of extensive outdoor cooking.

There are various weight ranges at which retailers can purchase ribs. They are called 2 lb and down, 3 lb and down, 3 to 5 lb, 5 to 7 lb, and 7 lb and up. They are generally purchased from packers or wholesalers in 30-lb boxes. The smaller the rib in weight, the more costly they are to the retailer. The most popular type of sparerib used by the retail trade is the 3 lb and down. These ribs are generally removed from the meat-type hog (barrow and gilt class) in the weight range of 200–220 lb at the time of slaughter. The 2 lb and down are generally purchased by the hotel, restaurant, and institu-tional trades. (See Fig. 5.7 for merchandising spareribs.)

Pork Stomach

Packers generally freeze pork stomachs in various container sizes. Some stomachs can be purchased in the fresh state. The bulk of the pork stomachs is merchandised to sausage manufacturers to be used for the production of a cheaper grade of sausage. The stomachs are considered to be quite a delicacy within certain ethnic groups. They are often called "hog maws."

Pork Melts

Melts are long, reddish, spongy organs which are the spleen of the animals. The hog spleen is sold mainly for the manufacture of dog food. Government-inspected houses are not permitted to use hog melts in sausage items. Pork lungs fall into this category and are also used for dog food.

Following are some reasons that reflect the advantages for including miscellaneous specialty pork items in the overall merchandising program of a specialty meat shop, chain store, or supermarket:

1. They are processed from superior quality hogs.
2. They are handled with extra care and with the highest degree of sanitation. They are also chilled to the proper temperature in the quickest possible manner.
3. They provide for a greater variety of selection by the consumer.
4. They are generally packaged attractively.
5. They are recognized as being rich source of vitamins and minerals (consumer education required as a phase of merchandising).
6. They offer good food value at reasonable cost.
7. They are particularly healthful as a part of the overall diet.

Section II: LAMB

UNIT 6: Lamb Carcass Classes, Grades, and Cuts

Lamb is a product of the sheep family (ovine species). Generally, the principal purpose of raising sheep is two-fold: the production of meat and the production of wool. In wool-producing countries, sheep are raised primarily for the wool and the by-product is mutton. In the United States, sheep are raised primarily for meat and the by-product is wool. There are numerous breeds of sheep. Some breeds are more productive in wool growth, while others are more productive in meat (carcass) development. Most breeds of lamb originated in the British Isles and were exported to this country.

College and university animal-husbandry experts, farmers, and ranchers are consistently improving breeds to produce lambs with heavier legs, fuller backs, and shorter bodies. Although lamb is considered to be one of the most delicious of meats, many people in the United States have never eaten or tasted lamb. It is estimated that ⅔ of the sheep population is raised west of the Mississippi and that ⅔ of the meat derived from sheep is consumed east of the Mississippi, especially in the New England States. Sheep are marketed during the entire year depending upon the geographic location of the country. Sheep are generally raised in the Northwest, Southwest, and Corn Belt regions of the country. This accounts for the availability of sheep throughout the year.

The slaughtering of sheep is similar to that of other types of livestock slaughter. The animal is stunned and then it is stuck (throat cut) to allow the bleeding of the animal. Kosher slaughter of sheep is similar except that the animal is stuck in a shackle-hung position without stunning. (The animal is in a live state, not unconscious.) After the animal is bled, it is then pelted (skin removed) and the head severed at the atlas joint. The animal is then eviscerated (removal of the internal organs) and placed in coolers for later distribution to wholesalers. They are also sold directly to retailers either in carcass form, primal and subprimal form, or processed into fabricated cuts. These merchandising and distribution practices will vary with packing house procedures. It has been found that meat inspectors condemn fewer lamb and mutton carcasses than any other class of livestock inspected under federal regulations. It is indicative of general good health of the animal as well as careful raising.

CLASSES

Sheep are generally classified by age. There are three classes of sheep: the lamb, the yearling mutton, and mutton.

Lamb

Lamb carcasses are derived from the young of the sheep family (ovine species). Lamb carcasses always have break joints on the lower foreshank bone (see Fig. 6.1). The rib bones are narrow, the color of the lean is light red, and there is a considerable amount of redness in the shank bones. However, lambs can have break joints up to 14 months of age. Young lambs, approximately 5 to

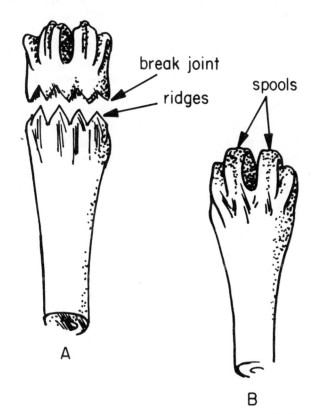

FIG. 6.1. AGE DIFFERENCE IN LAMB CARCASSES SHOWS IN LOWER FORESHANK BONE: A BREAK JOINT (A) IN YOUNG LAMB AND A SPOOL JOINT (B) IN OLD LAMB

A—In young carcasses when the foot is removed, the lower foreshank bone will display distinct ridges at the cartilaginous junction. B—In old and mature carcasses when the foot is removed, the lower foreshank bone will display distinct spools. The cartilaginous junction has ossified.

6 months of age at time of slaughter, are the most popular class of sheep for marketing.

Lamb is generally classified by age and weight. There are three classes of lamb.

1. A baby, or hothouse lamb, is approximately 2 months of age. They weigh between 20 and 40 lb and are sold with the pelt on (hog dressed) to protect the bloom and prevent excessive shrinkage. Hothouse lambs have a very pale, pink color of lean and have very red, bloody, and deep ridges at the break joint. Many ethnic groups purchase these lambs for their yearly festival occasions. The meat furnished from these lambs is very tender and delicate in flavor.

2. Spring lambs are approximately 5 to 7 months of age. They weigh between 40 and 50 lb and are generally fed on milk, pasture, grain, and hay. They are usually marketed in the spring and summer. Their break joints are red and moist. The lean is a pale pink in color. Within the category of spring lamb, there is a special class called "genuine spring lamb," which is similar to regular spring lamb except for the fact that it is younger in age. These are usually marketed from March to May, and sometimes beyond into the summer, depending upon the region of the country it comes from. These lambs are generally from 3 to 5 months of age and weigh between 30 and 45 lb. They are mainly fed on milk and are often referred to as "milk-fed" lambs.

3. Lambs are approximately 7 months to 1 yr in age. They average in weight between 50 and 65 lb. They are marketed in the fall and winter, and are sometimes referred to as winter lambs. The color of the lean is slightly dark pink. The rib bones are moderately red, and the break joints are rather dry and hard.

Yearling Mutton

Yearling mutton carcasses are derived from the more matured animals of the sheep family. The flesh from these matured carcasses is generally called lamb and merchandised as lamb. In reality, since the age span between the yearling mutton and mutton is short, the flesh borders on the mutton side. Yearling mutton carcasses either have break joints or "spool" joints on the lower fore-shank bone. The rib bones are moderately wide and the lean meat is of a slightly darker red color. They have small traces of red in the rib and shank bones. Yearling mutton will approach the yearling state at approximately from 10 to 12 months of age. At this point, the characteristics of the flesh begin to change. If it has a break joint, it is whiter and more brittle, and also dry. Young lambs have

moist, red break joints. Yearlings are rarely marketed. They are generally held for reproduction purposes.

Mutton

Mutton carcasses are derived from the old and matured of the sheep family. Mutton carcasses always have "spool" joints on the lower foreshank bone. The rib bones are wide and the color of the lean meat is dark red. The rib bones and shank bones are devoid of any red color. Mutton carcasses are generally 20 months or more of age. They have large abdominal cavities, and heavier shoulders and necks. The flesh from these carcasses is rarely, if ever, found in retail stores.

Mutton carcasses are classified according to sex. Sex is an important factor in the classification of mutton. The age of these animals from which the carcasses are obtained is 20 months or more. Wether carcasses are superior to the ewe and buck carcasses.

1. Wether carcasses are males from the more matured of the sheep family. They were generally castrated in the lamb stage. They are distinguishable from ewe and buck carcasses by the presence of cod fat, heavy bone structure, a thicker fleshing, and even form of conformation.

2. Ewe carcasses are females from the more matured of the sheep family which have borne one or more lambs. They have wider pelvics and larger abdominal cavities. Their necks and shanks are more slender than that of buck or wether carcasses.

3. Buck carcasses are derived from the uncastrated, older male of the sheep family that has been used for breeding purposes. They are heavy in the shoulder and neck, have large bones, and no cod fat is present in the flank region.

GRADES

The value of a lamb carcass depends chiefly upon two factors: the quality of the lean and quantity of retail cuts that the carcass yields.

USDA quality grades for lamb are Prime, Choice, Good, Utility, and Cull. These grades are reliable nationwide guides to lamb eating quality, tenderness, juiciness, and flavor. Since 1969, the USDA has established "yield" grades. These provide a nationally uniform method of identifying carcasses for differences in cutability and the yields of closely-trimmed, boneless, retail cuts from the leg, loin, hotel rack, and shoulder.

For further information concerning grades of lamb, the following booklets prepared by the Agricultural Marketing Service, U.S. Department of Agriculture, are available from Superintendent of

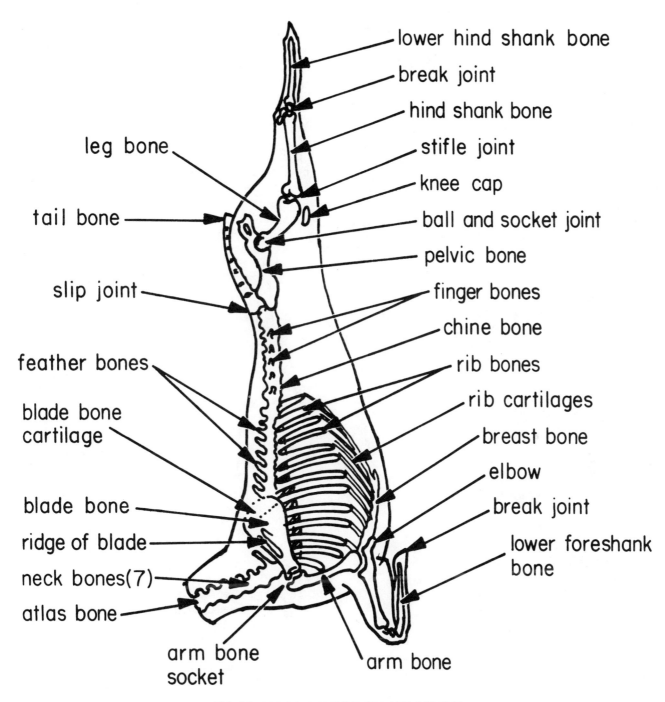

lower hind shank bone

break joint

hind shank bone

stifle joint

knee cap

ball and socket joint

pelvic bone

finger bones

chine bone

rib bones

rib cartilages

breast bone

elbow

break joint

lower foreshank bone

leg bone

tail bone

slip joint

feather bones

blade bone cartilage

blade bone

ridge of blade

neck bones(7)

atlas bone

arm bone socket

arm bone

FIG. 6.2. BONE STRUCTURE OF LAMB CARCASS

Documents, U.S. Government Printing Office, Washington, D.C. 20402: *Official United States Standards for Grades of Lamb, Yearling Mutton, and Mutton Carcasses*, booklet No. *123*; and *USDA Yield Grades for Lamb*, booklet *52*.

LAMB AND MUTTON IMPORTS

Due to the increased amount of imports from New Zealand and Australia, some lamb products (mostly lamb legs in a frozen state) are found in the display cases of many chain stores and supermarkets. The increase in imports from 1964 to 1970 ranged from 42.2 million pounds to 82.3 million pounds in lamb and mutton. A large portion of this meat is derived from mutton carcasses. It is estimated that, of all the lamb and mutton imported into this country, only 30% represents lamb. Most of the imports which are mainly in a boneless, frozen form are purchased by packers

and used for processed meats. This includes beef, veal, lamb, mutton, and pork from various countries.

Wholesalers engaged in the processing of portion control cuts may purchase some of the imported lamb for distribution to retailers. They generally process lamb legs into portion control cuts, depending upon contract bids. They generally bone the legs, seam out the individual muscles, and cut them into squares. They are marinated and then the cubes of lamb are placed with various cut vegetables on skewers. These units are then frozen and boxed for shish kebab in accordance with contract bids and specificiations

Many chains and supermarkets have advertised imported lamb legs at a savings to the consumer. The general public, especially those consumers who are partial to lamb, prefer American-grown lamb to the imported lamb. There are a number of factors which can make a decided difference between the two types of lamb. These are: the breed of lamb,

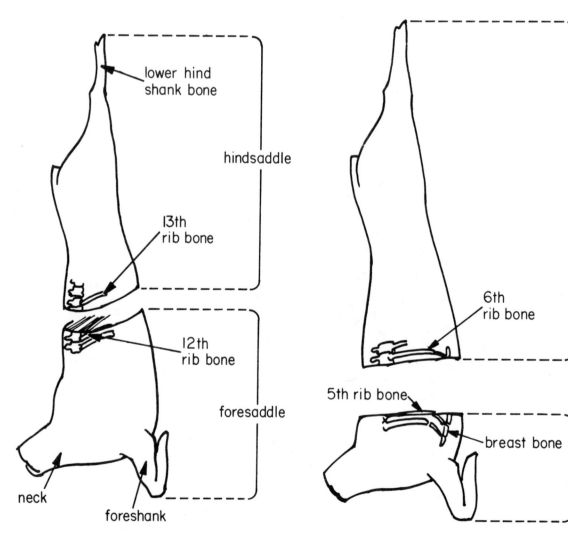

FIG. 6.3. HINDSADDLE AND FORESADDLE OF LAMB   FIG. 6.4. LAMB CHUCK AND LONG HINDSADDLE

the feed, and the region of the country in which the lamb was raised. Imported lamb may have a wild, gamey taste. The color of the lean is darker and the texture is coarser. The most important factor distinguishable to the American consumer is the taste. A number of chains and supermarkets have discontinued the purchase of imported lambs because of these factors. Where this is merchandising policy, the chains and supermarkets now advertise lamb legs as "American grown."

WHOLESALE CUTS

Wholesale cuts and retail cuts from the lamb carcass are somewhat similar. The variations often depend upon the processing practices of the packer, the wholesaler, or the retail meat cutter. The best and most economical manner of purchasing lamb is in its carcass form. Most meat men refer to this method of purchase as straight lamb. Many retailers often purchase additional wholesale cuts depending upon merchandising factors (special sales) and consumer demand. Stores will vary in their purchases. The following are variations of the manner in which the packer and wholesaler will break up lamb carcasses for retailers (see Fig. 6.2 for the bone structure of the lamb carcass).

Hindsaddle and Foresaddle of Lamb

The lamb carcass is split between the 12th and 13th rib bone. The foresaddle is that portion of the carcass containing the neck and the foreshanks, and consists of all the meat from the 12th rib, including the 12th rib, and down to the neck. The hindsaddle consists of all the meat from the 13th rib bone, and including the 13th rib bone, to the lower hind shank bone (see Fig. 6.3). Each part represents 50% of the lamb carcass.

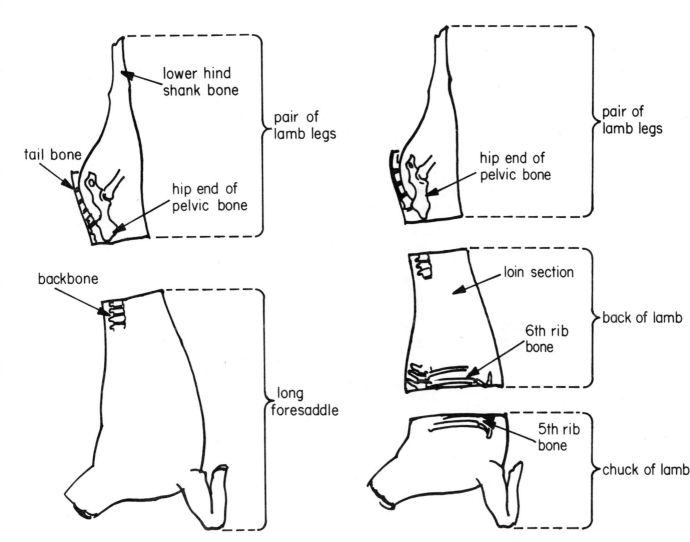

FIG. 6.5. PAIR OF LAMB LEGS AND LONG FORESADDLE

FIG. 6.6. THREE-WAY BREAKDOWN OF LAMB CARCASS

Lamb Chuck and Long Hindsaddle

The lamb carcass is cut between the 5th and 6th rib bone and the breast bone. The lamb chuck is that portion composed of the neck and foreshanks and represents approximately 33% of the carcass. The long hindsaddle is that portion from the 6th rib bone to the lower hind shank bone. This portion represents approximately 66% of the carcass (see Fig. 6.4).

Pair of Lamb Legs and Long Foresaddle

The lamb carcass is cut at the end of the pelvic bone (hip) through the backbone. The legs are that portion of the carcass containing the lower hind shank bone which represents approximately 33% of this portion of the carcass. The long foresaddle of lamb is that portion from the end of the

pelvic bone to the neck. This portion represents approximately 67% of the carcass (see Fig. 6.5).

Three-Way Break Down of the Lamb Carcass

The carcass is cut between the 5th and 6th rib bones. Another cut is made at the end of the pelvic bone. The part containing the neck is called a chuck of lamb. The part containing the lower hind shank bones is called a pair of lamb legs. The center part containing the ribs and loin is called a back of lamb. The back of lamb will represent approximately 34% of the total carcass (see Fig. 6.6).

Four-Way Break Down of Lamb Carcass

The carcass is cut between the 5th and 6th rib bones. Another cut is made between the 12th and 13th rib bones. Still another cut is made at the

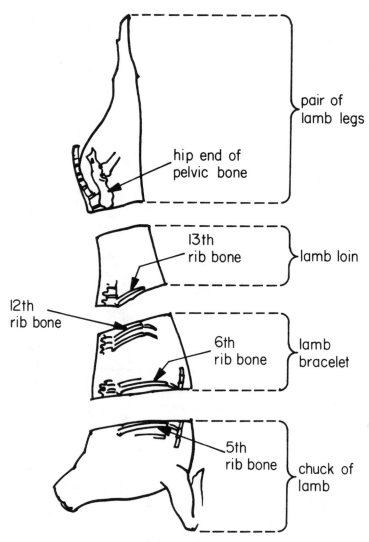

FIG. 6.7. FOUR-WAY BREAKDOWN OF LAMB CARCASS

end of the pelvic bone. The part containing the neck is called the chuck of lamb. It will represent approximately 33% of the total carcass. The part containing the ribs is called the bracelet. It will represent approximately 17% of the total carcass. The part containing the 13th rib bone is called the loin. It will represent approximately 17% of the total carcass. The part containing the lower hind shank bones is called the legs. It will represent approximately 33% of the total carcass (see Fig. 6.7).

Five-Way Breakdown of a Lamb Carcass

The rattle is removed from the carcass by cutting 1 in. from the elbow across the arm bone and through the rib bones which includes the flank of the animal. This will represent approximately 15%

of the total carcass. The remainder of the carcass is called a trimmed lamb. The next cut is between the 5th and 6th rib bone. This portion is called the square cut chuck. It is approximately 25% of the total carcass. Another cut is made between the 12th and 13th rib bone. This portion contains 14 rib bones and is called the hotel rack. The next cut is made at the end of the pelvic bone to separate the loin and the legs. The portion with the lower hind shank bone is called a pair of legs. The other portion which has the kidneys is called the loin (see Fig. 6.8).

Processing the Carcass into a Pair of Legs, Trimmed Back, and Chuck with Wings On

The legs are removed by cutting at the end of the pelvic bone (hip end). A cut is made between the 5th and 6th rib bones down to approximately

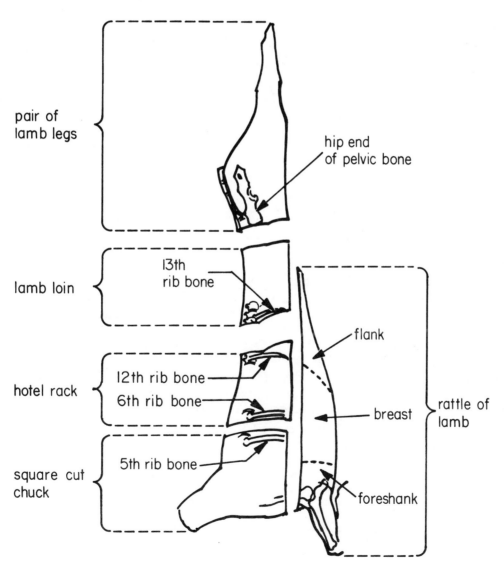

FIG. 6.8. FIVE-WAY BREAKDOWN OF LAMB CARCASS

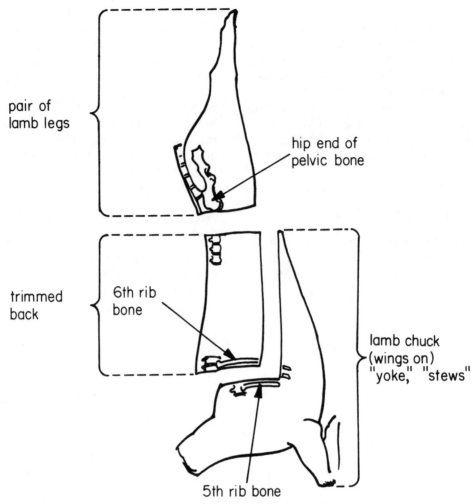

pair of
lamb legs

hip end of
pelvic bone

trimmed
back

6th rib
bone

lamb chuck
(wings on)
"yoke," "stews"

5th rib bone

FIG. 6.9. PAIR OF LEGS, TRIMMED BACK, AND CHUCK WITH WINGS ON

1 in. from the elbow and then cut across the rib bones (parallel to the backbone) and includes the flank. This portion is called a chuck (wings on). It is sometimes referred to as a "yoke" or "stews." It will represent approximately 40% of the total carcass. The center portion is called a trimmed back. It consists of a hotel rack and loin and will represent approximately 27% of the total carcass (see Fig. 6.9).

There are other fabricated cuts which packers process and pack into cartons such as shanks, necks, or breasts. They also pack trimmed shoulders, legs oven-prepared, and portion control cuts for hotels, restaurants, and institutions. The type of cutting will vary from packer to packer. Wholesalers who do not engage in portion control cutting generally break down carcasses into saddles, backs, legs, loins, bracelets, racks, and chucks. These are the main items retailers are interested in purchasing.

UNIT 7: Lamb Legs

Merchandisers of meat, with specific emphasis upon lamb, have found that lamb legs are not quite as readily accepted as other meats by consumers for a number of understandable reasons. These may be related to a lack of knowledge in cooking of lamb dishes, the weight and size of the lamb leg, purchase cost, or it may be attributed to the meat cutter who is not skilled and knowledgeable and is unable to assist the consumer in the selection of a cut of lamb. Skill is necessary for the processing of various types of cuts which can be derived from lamb legs. Meat managers may also be at fault for not displaying variety cuts or permitting meat cutters to process a greater variety of retail cuts from the lamb legs. Managers should be flexible and innovative in order to improve the tonnage of lamb sales in their stores. Of course, not all cuts will move equally and persistence may be necessary in merchandising in order to encourage the consumer to purchase variety lamb cuts and to prepare a variety of lamb dishes.

Chain stores and supermarkets rarely cut lamb legs into a variety of different cuts or prepare boneless cuts. This may be due to the high cost of labor and the challenge of competitive pricing. Meat department managers must realize that if they introduce different cuts from lamb legs they will be merchandising new retail cuts which may not be classified as competitive items. This unit will deal with this type of merchandising in order to assist the meat cutter and the cook in the preparation of various types of cuts from the lamb legs.

Lamb legs represent approximately ⅓ of the carcass. Examine the bone structure of the lamb leg carefully (see Fig. 7.1). This will assist you later in the unit when boning the lamb leg. Most retailers purchase extra lamb legs from the wholesaler or directly from the packer. Lamb legs come in pairs. Retailers refer to them as legs of lamb. Chain stores and supermarkets have their own methods of preparing oven-ready legs. This will be further explained as you progress through this unit. Return to Fig. 7.1 and re-examine the bone structure carefully once again. The lamb leg consists of the lower hind shank bone, the hind shank bone, the leg bone (round bone), the knee cap, the pelvic bone, and the tail bone. As you can see, most of the bone is located in the sirloin end of the leg (butt end). This portion is the most difficult to merchandise because of its bone structure. Many consumers are disappointed when carving this section of the leg after it is cooked. This is primarily due to the lack of knowledge of the bone structure of the leg.

Chain stores and supermarkets generally merchandise lamb legs by selling them whole, cut in half, the sirloin end cut into chops, or center slices cut for lamb steaks. They also merchandise shank and but ends. Rarely do they bone lamb legs or parts of the leg. This is often considered as poor processing and merchandising practice. Skilled meat cutters are usually fast and efficient when boning lamb legs. This will provide the consumer with a greater variety of cuts from the lamb leg. It may ease the task of menu planning for the consumer with inclusion of meat dishes made with lamb. The following is a list of methods directly related to the merchandising of lamb legs:

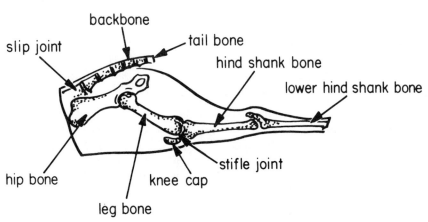

FIG. 7.1. BONE STRUCTURE OF THE LEG

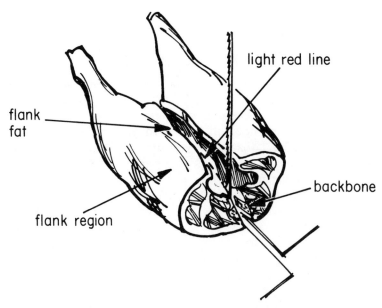

FIG. 7.2. SEPARATE A PAIR OF LEGS ON THE BAND SAW FOLLOWING
LIGHT RED SEPARATION LINE

Separating a Pair of Legs

Lamb legs can be split with a hand saw or a power saw. It is advisable to split lamb legs with the tail side down facing the table. In this position you can see a small, red line on the fat close to the tail bone and extending slightly in the direction of the backbone. This natural structure provides a line which, if followed on the band saw, will cut the legs evenly down the center of the bone (see Fig. 7.2).

Merchandising the Whole Leg (Bone-in)

Retail merchants should have a system for merchandising legs of different weights (small, medium, and large). Small legs should be merchandised whole with the bone in. Medium legs can be merchandised whole, cut in half, partially sliced with bone-in. Large legs may be processed as a bone-in item or processed into a variety of boneless retail cuts. Small legs average about 6–7 lb in weight. Medium legs are in the range of 8–9 lb. Large legs average about 10–12 lb. The methods employed by retailers may involve different procedures and practices in processing and merchandising the various lamb legs. The variety of cuts and their sales potential will determine the best methods and techniques to be used. There are no set rules and regulations for merchandising legs.

Method No. 1

1. Place the leg on the bench with the outside surface facing the bench and the bone side up.
2. Scrape with the heel of the boning knife toward the break joint between the hind shank bone and the lower hind shank bone (see Fig. 7.3).
3. Place the lower hind shank bone at the edge of the bench and push down on the lower hind shank bone to crack the joint at the break joint (see Fig. 7.4).

   Note: Some retailers will simply saw through the lower hind shank bone. Some stores will either place the bone in the same package with the lamb leg or tuck the bone under the leg. This is poor merchandising practice because it adds unnecessary weight and increases consumer cost. Remove the bone in its entirety and discard it for regular disposal later, unless the consumer requests the bone.

4. Saw through the tail and pelvic bone on the butt end up to the ball and socket joint, which are approximately 1 in. apart (see Fig. 7.5).

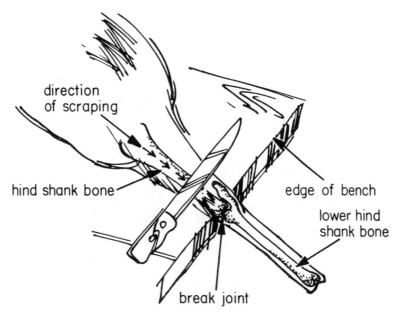

FIG. 7.3. SCRAPE EXPOSED BONE TOWARD THE BREAK JOINT

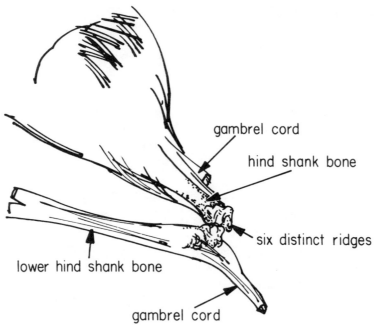

FIG. 7.4. EXPOSED VIEW OF BREAK JOINT IN HIND SHANK BONE

Caution: Keep your fingers clear from the path of the blade. Bring the lamb leg up to the blade and, after you have felt the blade passing through the bone, release the leg back to the table. Do not force the leg or push the leg into the blade.

Note: Trimming the pelvic fat and cod fat is a matter of store merchandising practice. It is advisable to remove approximately ½ of the pelvic fat and cod fat before cutting through the tail and pelvic bone.

5. Place a clear wrap over the fat surface of the leg exposing the grade stamp to the consumer.

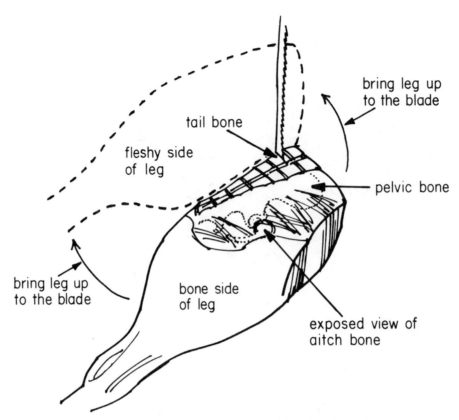

FIG. 7.5. SAW THROUGH THE TAIL AND PELVIC BONE

Note: If the hind shank bone shows the ridges of the break joint, it is labeled as a French lamb leg. If the hind shank bone is sawed, it is labeled as a regular lamb leg.

Method No. 2

1. Remove the lower hind shank as in method No. 1.
2. Cut 3 to 4 chops from the sirloin end (butt) approximately ¾ in. in thickness. Trim the chops well (see Fig. 7.6).

   Note: The chops can be merchandised separately or placed with the remainder of the leg and sold as a combination lamb leg. This is a matter of store merchandising practice (see Fig. 7.7).

Method No. 3

1. Remove the lower hind shank as employed in method No. 1.
2. Remove the shank portion of the leg by cutting through the stifle joint (see Fig. 7.8).

   Note: This shank is meatier than the foreshank and should merchandise readily. They may be cracked through the shank bone (see Fig. 7.9).

3. Cut through the tail and pelvic bone as described in step No. 3 in method No. 1.
4. Place clear wrap over the fat surface and label the leg as an American lamb leg.

Method No. 4

When merchandising halves, it is important to understand that if the processed halves do not have equal amounts of meat on each half there is usually some difficulty in merchandising. In most cases, the shank half is more desirable and sells

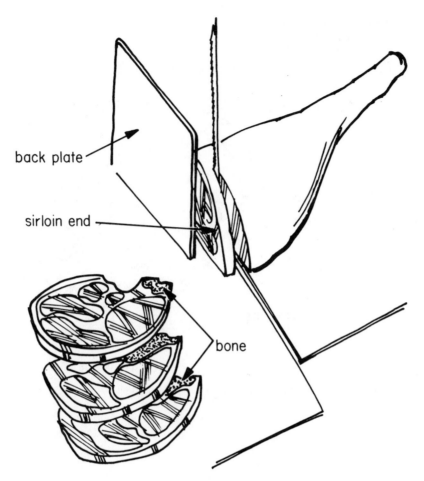

back plate

sirloin end

bone

FIG. 7.6. THREE OR FOUR SIRLOIN CHOPS MAY BE CUT FROM THE BUTT
END OF THE LEG

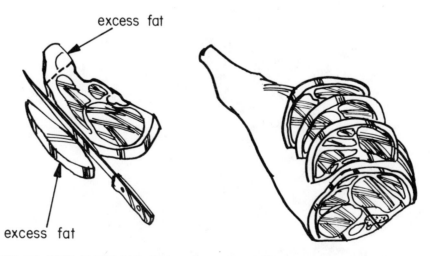

excess fat

excess fat

FIG. 7.7. TRIM CHOPS AND MERCHANDISE SEPARATELY OR PLACE WITH THE
WHOLE LEG AS SHOWN

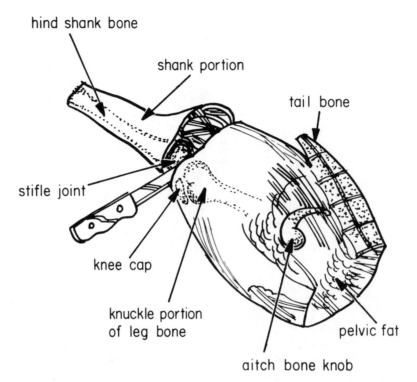

FIG. 7.8. FOR AMERICAN STYLE LEG OF LAMB, REMOVE LOWER HIND
SHANK

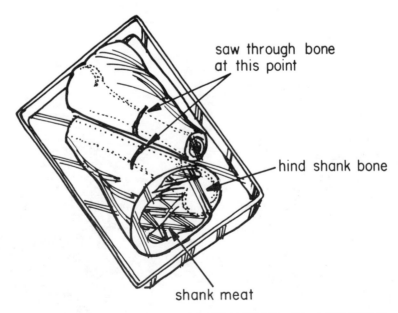

FIG. 7.9. MERCHANDISE   SHANKS   SEPARATELY   IN   ATTRACTIVE
PACKAGE

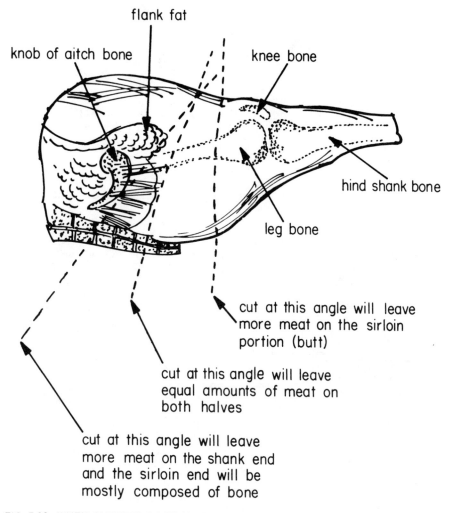

flank fat

knob of aitch bone

knee bone

hind shank bone

leg bone

cut at this angle will leave
more meat on the sirloin
portion (butt)

cut at this angle will leave
equal amounts of meat on
both halves

cut at this angle will leave
more meat on the shank end
and the sirloin end will be
mostly composed of bone

FIG. 7.10. WHEN CUTTING A LEG IN HALF, ANGLE OF CUT WILL DETERMINE PRO-
PORTION OF MEAT IN EITHER PIECE

faster. The butt half is usually somewhat slower in being merchandised and may have to be reprocessed into other retail cuts. This is a costly practice. The angle of cut which is made through the leg bone is important. Most of the difficulty may be in the fact that many meat cutters may cut close to the exposed view of the knob of the aitch bone. This leaves the butt half mostly composed of bone. Consumers will be discouraged if they purchase this cut and, as a result, you may lose sales in the future purchase of lamb legs in any form. The reverse may also occur if too much meat is left on the sirloin end and little meat left on the shank end. See Fig. 7.10 for the approximate angle to cut legs in half.

Method No. 5

1. Remove the lower hind shank bone.
2. Starting at the butt end, cut chops approximately ¾ in. in thickness down to the beginning of the knuckle portion of the leg bone. Trim the sirloin chops well (see Fig. 7.11).

   Note: Chops cut from the butt end should be labeled lamb sirloin chops—leg; and the remainder of the chops from the leg can be labeled lamb steaks—leg, or lamb chops—leg. Some meat cutters will cut the steaks somewhat

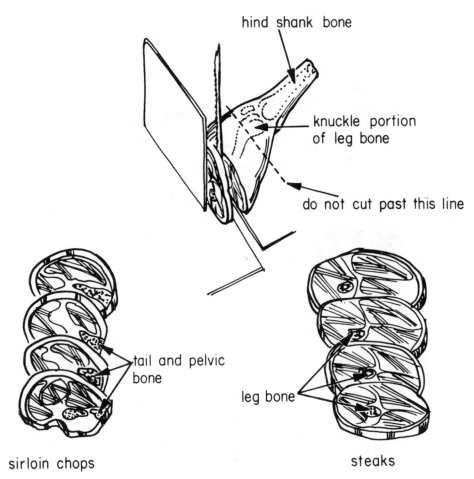

FIG. 7.11. THE ENTIRE LEG MAY BE CUT INTO CHOPS AND STEAKS

thicker (1 in. in thickness). It is important to remember that steaks retail at a higher selling price than chops.

Note: If difficulty arises when merchandising shanks, it is advisable to bone the shanks (see Fig. 7.12). Use the boneless shank meat to cut into cubes for stew or shish kebabs. They may also be ground with other trimmings from lamb and made into a lamb patty or a lamb cube steak.

Merchandising the Whole Leg (Boneless)

In processing the whole lamb leg, many meat cutters do not show a preference for using the tunneling method of boning because they are of the opinion that too much time is consumed when using this method. This is a rather false premise in that an experienced meat cutter can bone legs with the tunneling method as rapidly as meat cutters that usually cut through the lean meat to remove the leg bone. An important factor worthy of consideration is that when lamb legs are opened up by cutting through the meat to remove the bones, and not tunneled, tieing the leg often becomes difficult. In addition, the resulting leg roast will not be as attractive as the leg that was tunneled. The boneless meat becomes loose and sloppy and requires more stitching than is necessary to form a perfect, rectangular shape. When carving after cooking, the slices will not be as attractive as a tunneled lamb leg. It is advisable for meat cutters to tunnel out the leg bone on a lamb leg to make a more attractive boned and tied leg for merchandising.

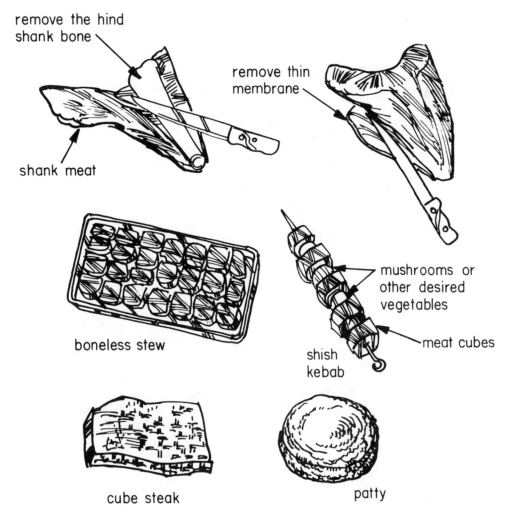

remove the hind shank bone

remove thin membrane

shank meat

boneless stew

mushrooms or other desired vegetables

shish kebab

meat cubes

cube steak

patty

FIG. 7.12. HIND SHANKS MAY BE BONED AND THE MEAT MERCHANDISED IN VARIOUS WAYS

Boning the Leg

1. Place the leg on the bench with the fleshy side down and the bone side up.

   Note: Do not remove the flank or flank fat at this point. The flank will be of assistance to you later on in the rolling and tieing procedure. This is particularly so when you are forming a rectangular shape before the actual rolling and tieing.

2. Loosen and lay back the tenderloin muscle along the side of the pelvic bone. Start with the tip of the boning knife at the knob end of the aitch bone (see Fig. 7.13).

   Caution: Do not cut too deep or you will score the sirloin muscle. Use only the tip of the knife.

   Note: This will expose the slip joint and the last finger bone for later removal.

3. Cut through the cartilage junction of the backbone (tail portion) located near the end of the hip bone (see Fig. 7.14). Push down with your thumb on the last vertebra to loosen it from the tail. Remove the bone with the boning knife by following the contour of the finger bone.

   Caution: Always cut in the direction the bench. Do not cut in upward strokes.

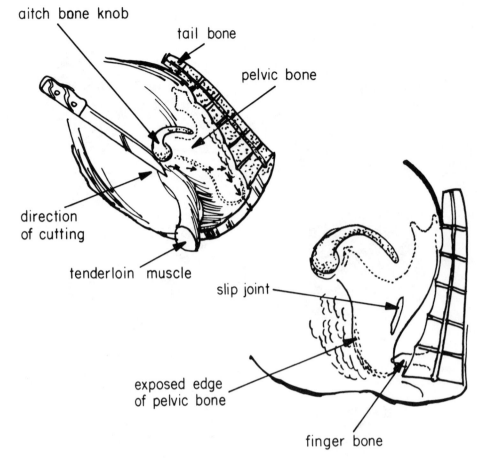

FIG. 7.13. LOOSEN TENDERLOIN MUSCLE TO EXPOSE SLIP JOINT

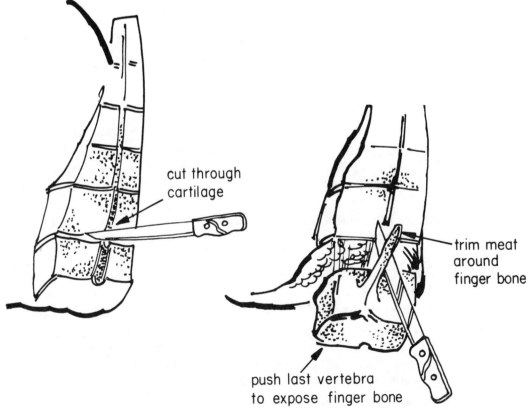

FIG. 7.14. HOW TO REMOVE LAST FINGER BONE FROM BUTT END OF LEG

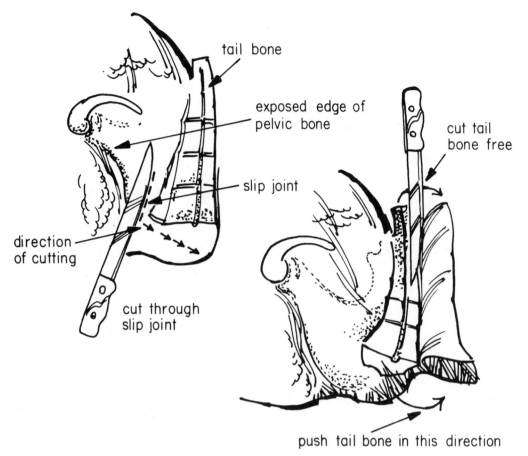

tail bone

exposed edge of
pelvic bone

slip joint

direction
of cutting

cut through
slip joint

cut tail
bone free

push tail bone in this direction

FIG. 7.15. CUT TAIL BONE FREE FROM LEG

Note: Some meat cutters will omit this step, because of haste, and leave all the meat attached to the finger bone. This practice is wasteful. However, it does exist because it is a matter of store practice in processing and merchandising.

4. Remove the oyster meat in the cavity of the aitch bone.

Note: These trimmings can be used for ground meat items or mixed with other lean cuts for cubed lamb steaks or patties. Some meat cutters feel that the amount is so small that it really does not pay to remove this portion. It is important to remember that there are 16 oz to each pound of meat and every ounce is vital to the merchandising of any meat item.

5. Cut through the slip joint keeping the cutting edge of the knife in the direction of the tail bone. Do not force the knife through. It should slide through very easily. If not, you are not cutting in the right direction toward the slip joint. Loosen all the meat from the tail portion and remove the bone (see Fig. 7.15).

Caution: Keep your free hand in back of the cutting edge of the knife while you are holding the leg in order to cut through the slip joint. Do not use force while doing so.

Note: Some meat cutters will remove the tail bone with the aitch bone. Again, this is a matter of store procedure and practice.

6. Cut close to the knob of the aitch bone keeping the tip of the boning knife against the bone. Cut down through the cord and through the ball and socket joint. Following the contour of the bone, use the tip of the knife to free the meat from the protruding edge of the pelvic bone (see Fig. 7.16).

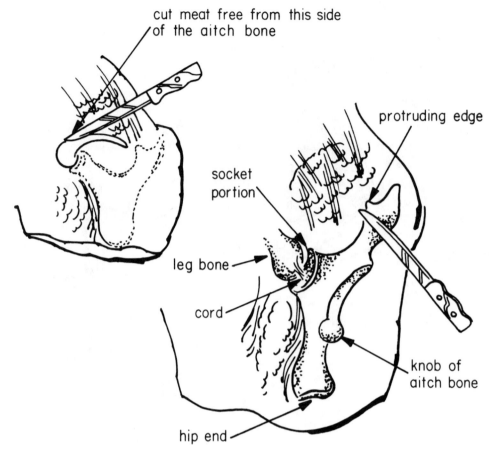

FIG. 7.16. CUT PELVIC BONE FREE FROM LEG

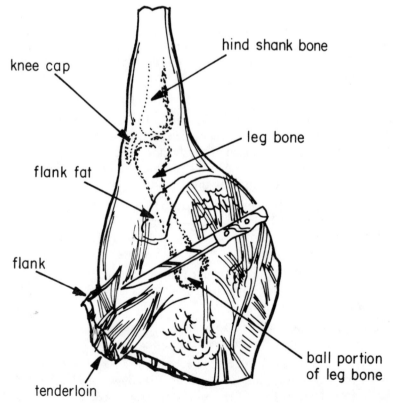

FIG. 7.17. CUT ALL MEAT FREE FROM BALL PORTION OF LEG BONE

Caution: Keep your fingers away from the cutting action of the knife.

Note: If the seam is caught at the ball and socket portion of the bone, the bone will pull freely from the meat at the hip end of the bone.

7. Loosen all the meat around the ball portion of the leg bone (see Fig. 7.17).

Note: Scrape with the heel of the knife in order to catch the seam around the leg bone.

8. Loosen the meat on each side of the hind shank bone, keeping the tip of the knife against the bone. Tunnel through on the knuckle portion of the leg bone. Scrape with the heel of the knife to catch the seam on this portion of the bone.

Note: Feel with your finger tips for the location of the knee cap. Cut around the knee cap before tunneling the knuckle portion of the leg bone (see Fig. 7.18).

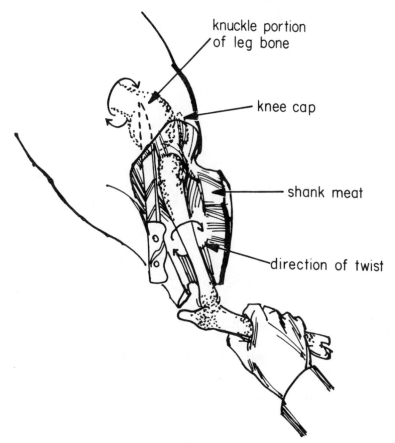

FIG. 7.18. TWIST LEG BONE FREE FROM MEAT

9. Holding the lower hind shank bone in your hand, twist and remove all the bones in one piece: the lower hind shank bone, the hind shank bone, the leg bone, and the knee cap.

Note: While you are pulling the bone from the cavity, some meat may adhere to the bone because the seam was not caught on the bone properly. If so, simply free the meat with the boning knife while you are pulling the bones from the cavity. This is done in a scraping fashion.

Tieing the Boneless Leg

1. Place the shank meat into the cavity of the leg bone as far as it will go.

Note: Use both thumbs to push the shank meat well into the cavity.

2. Place the stitch about 1 in. from the cavity into the leg and catch the shank meat with the needle. Straighten the needle so that it is parallel with the sirloin end and continue pushing the needle through to the opposite side of the leg. It will be approximately 1 in. away from the cavity. Repeat this with two or more stitches to close the cavity (see Fig. 7.19).

Caution: Keep your free hand away from the point of the needle.

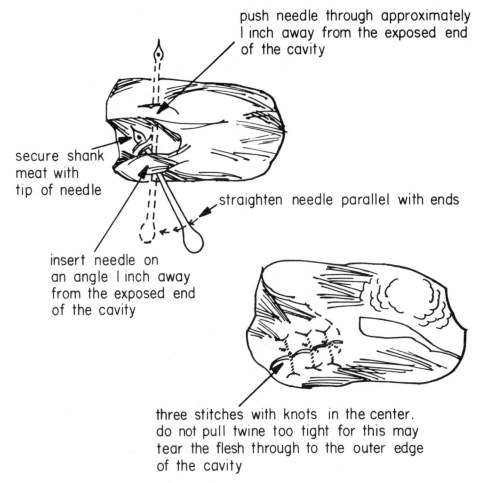

push needle through approximately I inch away from the exposed end of the cavity

secure shank meat with tip of needle

straighten needle parallel with ends

insert needle on an angle I inch away from the exposed end of the cavity

three stitches with knots in the center. do not pull twine too tight for this may tear the flesh through to the outer edge of the cavity

FIG. 7.19. HOW TO SECURE SHANK MEAT INTO CAVITY WHERE BONE WAS REMOVED

Note: It is important to see that both ends are parallel to each other in order to form a rectangular shape. Many chefs and cooks prefer this shape for cooking.

3. Place a guide string loosely around the leg. Put a knot at the bottom of the roast (see Fig. 7.20).

Note: Some meat cutters prefer to use a double guide string. This is a matter of store merchandising practice.

4. Start by placing cross strings at the thick end of the leg and parallel to the face of the lamb leg. Tie five evenly-spaced cross strings tightly around the leg. Keep the knots at the bottom of the leg. (See Fig. 7.21.)

Note: Boned and tied lamb legs that are large are often cut in half by some meat cutters. This is also a matter of store merchandising practice.

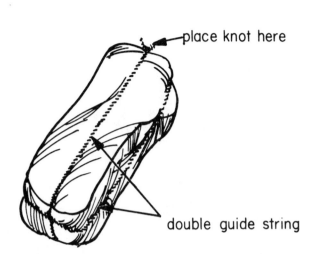

FIG. 7.20. PLACE DOUBLE GUIDE STRING AROUND
BONELESS LEG

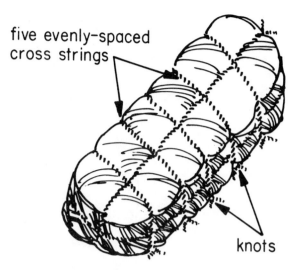

FIG. 7.21. FINISH TIEING WITH CROSS STRINGS
KNOTTED AT BOTTOM

Preparing A Semiboneless Leg

Very often, chain stores and supermarkets advertise an oven-ready lamb leg. Variations of this cut often confuse the consumer as well as the meat cutter and the chef. Some stores will remove the hind shank bone, tail bone, and pelvic bone while others may only remove the tail bone and hind shank bone.

The *Meat Buyer's Guide to Portion Control Meat Cuts*[1] lists a lamb leg (partially boneless) as a leg with the entire flank, all cod or udder fat, and exterior surface fat in excess of ½ in. as being removed. Pelvic bones and tail bones must also be removed. The shank bone must be removed at the stifle joint, and all the gambrel cord also removed.

The *Meat Buyer's Guide to Standardized Meat Cuts*[1] defines the semiboneless leg, as a leg, oven-prepared (single), as described above. Retail stores may use different methods to prepare a semiboneless leg. The following method is a simple procedure.

1. Follow steps No. 1 through No. 5 in boning the leg.
2. Loosen the meat from each side of the shank bone and cut through the stifle joint to free the bone.

 Caution: Keep fingers clear from the path of the knife.

3. Remove the flank and flank fat that is in excess of ½ in.

 Note: This leg can also be merchandised by employing the following added methods:
  (a) Remove the boneless sirloin portion by cutting vertically at a 90 degree angle using the exposed view of the round bone as the base of the angle (see Fig. 7.22).
  (b) Remove the shank meat at the end of the knuckle end of the leg bone.
  (c) The sirloin end and shank meat can be merchandised by cubing for shish kebabs, cutting for boneless stew, or sliced for lamb cube steaks or cutlets. (Refer back to Fig. 7.12.)
  (d) The center portion of the leg now has only one bone in the center (leg bone). This makes for an ideal roast for the consumer because it will be easy to slice and serve after cooking.

---

[1] Available from the National Association of Meat Purveyors, 120 S. Riverside Plaza, Chicago, Ill. 60606.

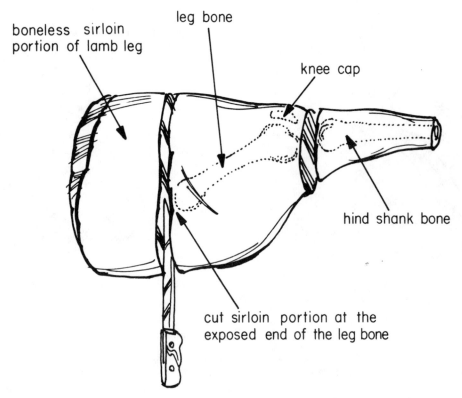

FIG. 7.22. REMOVE THE BONELESS SIRLOIN PORTION AND THE SHANK PORTION FROM THE LEG

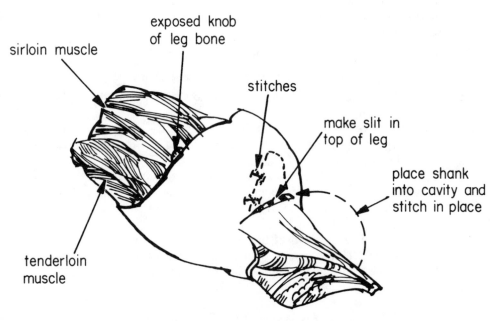

FIG. 7.23. STITCH SHANK MEAT INTO SLIT MADE ON TOP OF LEG

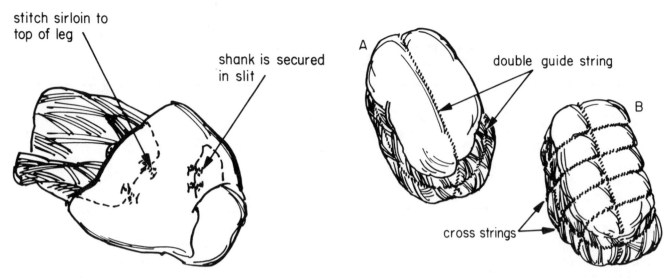

FIG. 7.24. STITCH SIRLOIN MEAT FROM OPPOSITE END ONTO TOP OF LEG AS SHOWN

FIG. 7.25. PLACE DOUBLE GUIDE STRING (A) AROUND LEG THEN TIE WITH CROSS STRINGS (B)

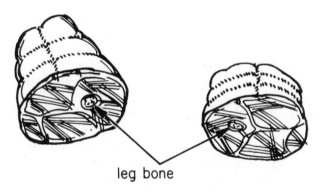

FIG. 7.26. A SEMIBONELESS LEG CUT IN HALF

Tieing the Semiboneless Leg

Refer back to steps No. 1, 2, and 3.

1. Cut a slit in the form of a pocket on the top portion of the leg (see Fig. 7.23).
2. Place the shank meat into the pocket and stitch.
3. Place the triangle end of the sirloin end under the leg and stitch into place (see Fig. 7.24).
4. Place a double guide string around the length of the leg (see Fig. 7.25A).
5. Tie evenly-placed cross strings around the leg. (See Fig. 7.25B.)

   Note: Large legs may be cut in half. There should be no problem in equalizing the meat on both ends. (See Fig. 7.26.)

UNIT 8: Lamb Chucks

The lamb chuck represents approximately 33% of the carcass. The chuck contains a large percentage of bones (see Fig. 8.1). The bone structure consists of the lower foreshank bone, the arm bone, the blade bone, the rib bones (5), the breast bone, the neck bones (7), the feather bones, and chine bone (back bones). When lamb chucks are removed from the carcass they should be cut between the 5th and 6th rib bones. Wholesalers will often merchandise chucks of lamb with only the first 4 rib bones instead of 5 rib bones. This would leave an extra rib on the hotel rack which commands a higher wholesale price. This practice is not always in effect at all times. Some wholesale meat cutters, working on a production basis, may sometimes in their haste miss the mark. The back of the hand, measuring from the base of the neck, is a common guide. Being one of the least expensive cuts from the lamb carcass, the chuck may not be considered as a very important factor in merchandising for some wholesalers or retailers. Some retailers may, when breaking down the lamb carcasses, cut a 4-rib chuck rather than a 5-rib in order to retail the fifth rib as a rib chop rather than as a shoulder chop. Rib lamb chops have a higher selling price than shoulder chops. This matter will be further developed in this unit.

Chain stores and supermarkets generally rely on one basic method of cutting lamb chucks. This may be based upon the cost of labor or that region of the country where consumers prefer this type of cut. Although there are many different principles involved in cutting lamb chucks, retailers generally cut lamb chucks into lamb chops and meat for lamb stews. This unit will provide you with a greater variety of lamb cuts from the chuck.

Increasing your lamb sales can be accomplished by increasing variations in cutting the chucks. Refer back to Fig. 8.1, to familiarize yourself with the bone structure. These bones may be the reason many consumers do not purchase cuts from chucks. Therefore, it is important for meat cutters to achieve skill and practical knowledge in the processing of boneless cuts derived from the chuck.

When chucks are split down the center of the backbone, the resulting two sides are called lamb shoulders. When the shank is removed by cutting 1 in. from the elbow and parallel with the backbone, the shoulder is then called a square cut shoulder. Some meat cutters prefer to remove the neck before splitting the lamb chuck into shoulders. This is a matter of store merchandising practices that are based upon consumer preferences. Many chain stores and supermarkets advertise retail cuts from the shoulder and a combination of cuts in various forms: such as bone-in whole, sliced chops with stew meat, sliced into chops and tied into a roast, and sometimes chops with a lamb shank piece for potting. Most consumers prefer to purchase meat items with little bone or no bone at all, and with most of the excess fat removed from the items they are purchasing. It is important to remember that if lamb is merchandised properly, it will mean more sales tonnage for the store. The following are a few suggested methods for merchandising chucks (bone-in and boneless).

Splitting the Chuck into Two Shoulders

It is customary for the operator of the band saw to determine the method to be employed in splitting lamb chucks. Some meat cutters are reluctant to try using their own innovative methods. Other meat cutters are more flexible and will experiment to improve cutting efficiency. In all methods and techniques of cutting, *safety* should be the first and important concern of the band saw operator. Hazardous short cuts should be eliminated. Some meat cutters prefer to remove the foreshanks before cutting the chuck down the center of the backbone (see Fig. 8.2). Some factors generally given serious consideration before cutting are the need for more chops and stew meat in the display case or the need based primarily upon only one of these items. The meat cutter may only remove the shank and necks. He may not need stew meat or chops, but may need roasts with the bone in, or boneless, or combination lamb sales items. In this case, he may then split the chuck down the center of the backbone without removing any of the shanks or necks (see Fig. 8.3). The meat cutter may also be limited because he may have to follow store merchandising practices and procedures.

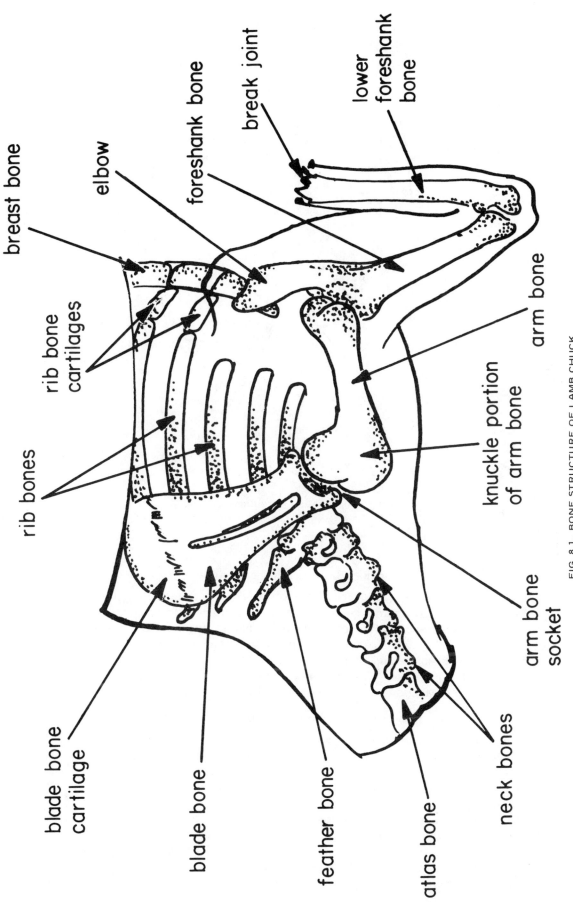

breast bone

elbow

foreshank bone

break joint

lower foreshank bone

rib bone cartilages

rib bones

blade bone cartilage

blade bone

feather bone

atlas bone

neck bones

arm bone socket

knuckle portion of arm bone

arm bone

FIG. 8.1. BONE STRUCTURE OF LAMB CHUCK

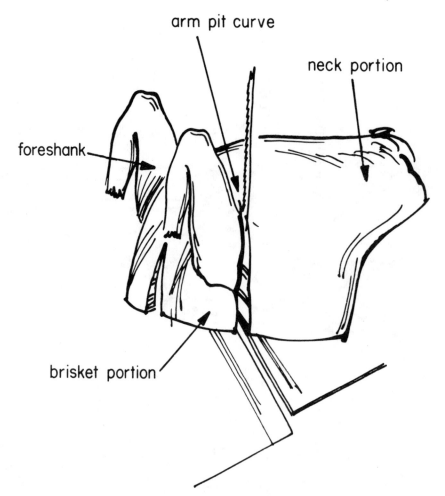

FIG. 8.2. CUT FORESHANKS FROM CHUCK

Cutting Chops From the Shoulder

Before chops can be sliced from the shoulder, the shank must be removed. Methods will vary in accordance with consumer demand and store merchandising practices. It is advisable to remove the shanks about ½ in. from the elbow joint. This will prevent the shank from having a bony appearance. If the shank is cut close to the elbow, the shank and brisket piece will separate. Some stores merchandise these two pieces together. Meat cutters generally use the arm pit, (the curve) and cut parallel to the backbone in order to remove the shanks (see Fig. 8.4).

Cutting Arm Bone Shoulder Chops (Round-Bone)

Chain stores and supermarkets, especially those in the metropolitan New York area, label and advertise chops from the arm bone section as round-bone shoulder lamb chops. This is primarily due to the fact that the cross section of the arm bone in the chop is round in shape. Retailers generally remove three chops from the arm section of the shoulder. This will depend upon the thickness of the chop. If less than three chops are removed, the blade chops that are cut might have the appearance of a chop that resembles a long and bony chop that may be too large to serve as a single portion. If more than three chops are removed, the fourth and fifth chops will largely be composed of bone because you will be cutting into the knuckle portion of the arm bone. Refer back to Fig. 8.1 to re-examine the bone structure of the lamb chuck.

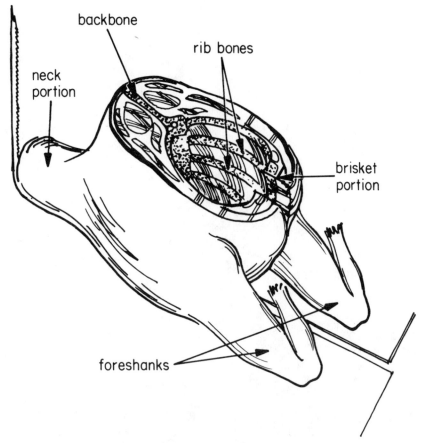

FIG. 8.3. SPLIT CHUCK DOWN THE CENTER OF THE BACKBONE

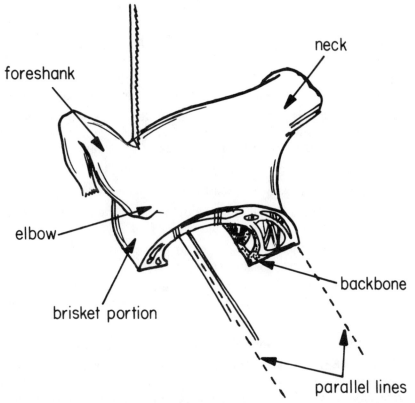

FIG. 8.4. CUT OFF FORESHANK AND BRISKET PORTION FROM SHOULDER

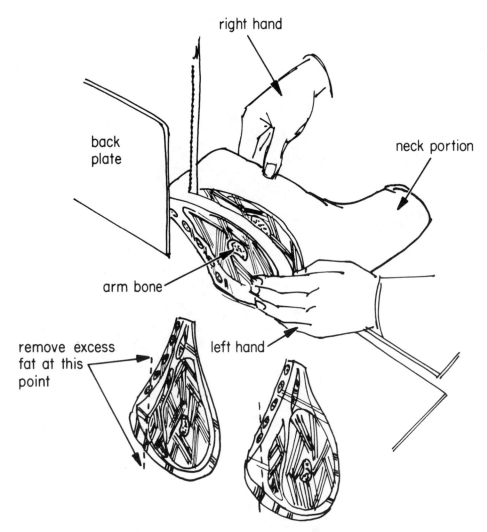

right hand

back
plate

neck portion

arm bone

remove excess
fat at this
point

left hand

FIG. 8.5 CUT ROUND-BONE (ARM BONE) CHOPS FROM SHOULDER

1. Place the square cut shoulder on the band saw with the bone side facing the table.

   Note: Some meat cutters prefer to cut the shoulder chops with the bone side up. For apprentice meat cutters, it is advisable to keep the flat surface of the meat being cut flush with the flat surface of the table.

2. Cut 3 round-bone chops approximately ¾-in. in thickness.

   Caution: Keep your fingers away from the path of the blade (see Fig. 8.5).

   Note: Use your left hand to guide the chop through the blade. Do not pull the chop through. Let the saw do the work. (See Fig. 8.5.)

3. It is advisable to trim these chops to remove excess fat in relation to store or management merchandising practices (see Fig. 8.5).

   Note: These chops can be merchandised separately at a higher retail price, or mixed with blade chops in various sized boats and in varying lamb combinations.

Cutting Blade Bone Shoulder Chops (Long-Bone)

The three round-bone chops should be removed before cutting the blade chops. The blade chops are often referred to as long-bone shoulder lamb chops. The number of chops removed is usually from 6 to 7 chops, depending upon the manner in which the chuck was removed from the carcass and the specific thickness of the chop. The amount of chops removed from a properly trimmed chuck will represent approximately 55% of the total chuck.

1. Place the square cut shoulder, minus round-bone chops, on the band saw with the bone side down. (See Fig. 8.6.)
2. Cut 6 to 7 blade chops approximately ¾-in. thick. (See Fig. 8.6.)

   Caution: Keep your fingers clear from the path of the blade.

   Note: Use your left hand to guide chops through the blade. It is advisable not to cut chops past the exposed portion of the arm bone on the arm bone side of the shoulder. (See Fig. 8.6.)

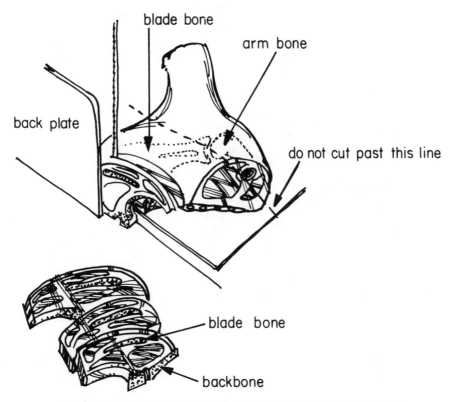

FIG. 8.6. CUT LONG BONE (BLADE BONE) CHOPS FROM SHOULDER

3. Trim the chops according to store merchandising specifications and place them in different sized boats for the consumer to make a selection.

   Note: These chops may also be merchandised for various lamb combination packages. This will be further developed in the unit stressing the merchandising of shanks and necks.

Merchandising Foreshanks and Necks

It is important to remember that in merchandising lamb a portion of the derived profits will stem from merchandising of the rough cuts from the carcass. These cuts are generally the foreshanks, breasts, necks, and flanks. Many retailers will remove this section of the carcass (rattle) when the shipment of lamb arrives. These cuts, plus the trimmings removed from the throat region, the skirt, and the hanging tender, should be merchandised before cutting the carcass into further retail cuts. This will eliminate an accumulation of rough cuts prior to the weekend. The consumer generally prefers to cook roasts for weekend meals. Ground meat and stew items are often prepared during other periods of the week. There are variations in cutting

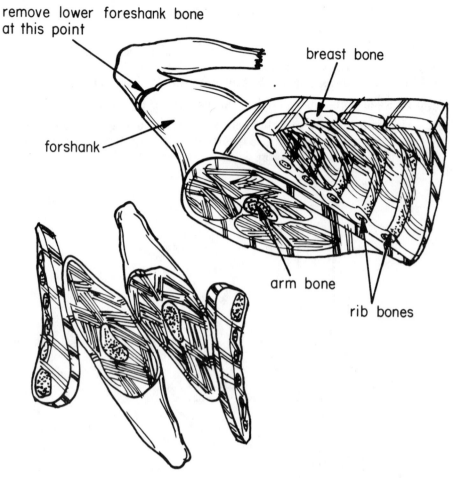

remove lower foreshank bone
at this point

breast bone

forshank

arm bone

rib bones

FIG. 8.7. TRIM OUT FORESHANKS AND PACKAGE TWO IN A BOAT WITH OPPOSITE
ENDS FACING EACH OTHER, AS SHOWN BELOW

lamb foreshanks and necks, bone-in or boneless. The following methods may be used and adjusted to meet customer requests.

Foreshanks

1. Remove the lower foreshank bone above the knee joint to make a shorter, thicker-looking shank (see Fig. 8.7).

   Note: Trim the excess fat and place two shanks in a boat with opposite ends facing each other. Some meat cutters may saw the shank bone and the brisket bone. (See Fig. 8.7.)

2. Follow the procedure in step No. 1 above. Remove the brisket portion of the foreshank through the webbing between the brisket and the shank (see Fig. 8.8).

   Note: The shanks are then trimmed and placed in a boat. These shanks should retail at a premium selling price (see Fig. 8.8).

3. The brisket piece may be sliced between the rib bones and merchandised as stew. This portion is composed mostly of bone and fat. It is advisable to separate the lean, thin muscle (brisket muscle) from the brisket bone at the natural seam. (See Fig. 8.9.)

4. Trim the brisket muscle pieces and place 2 or 3 pieces together. Put these through the mechanical tenderizing machine and then merchandise them as lamb cube steaks. (See Fig. 8.9.)

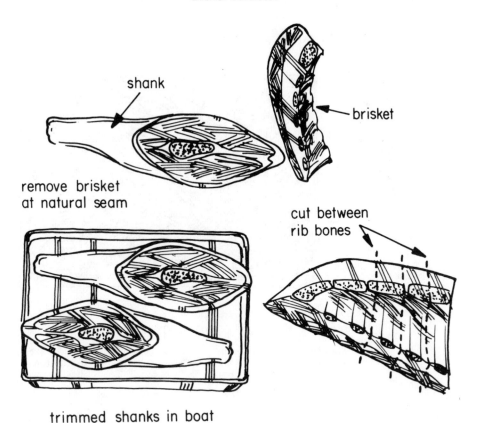

shank

brisket

remove brisket
at natural seam

cut between
rib bones

trimmed shanks in boat

FIG. 8.8. SEPARATE BRISKET PORTION AND TRIM SHANKS TO MERCHANDISE AT
PREMIUM PRICE

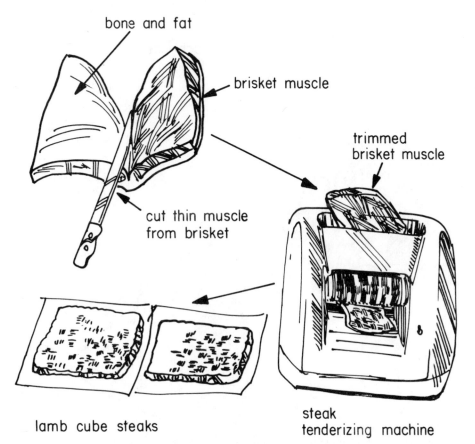

bone and fat

brisket muscle

trimmed
brisket muscle

cut thin muscle
from brisket

lamb cube steaks

steak
tenderizing machine

FIG. 8.9. THEN TRIM OUT BRISKET MUSCLE AND MERCHANDISE AS LAMB CUBE
STEAKS ON PATTY PAPERS, AS SHOWN BELOW

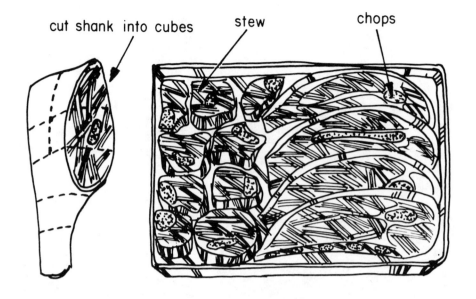

lamb combination

FIG. 8.10. SHANKS MAY BE MERCHANDISED AS STEW MEAT BY CUTTING INTO CUBES WITH BONE IN AND MAY ALSO BE MERCHANDISED THIS WAY IN COMBINATION WITH LAMB CHOPS, AS SHOWN BELOW

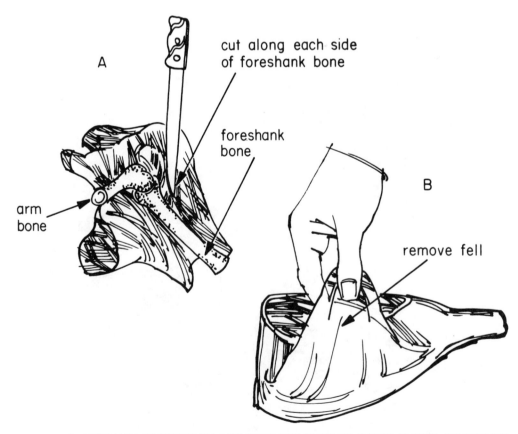

FIG. 8.11. SHANKS MAY BE BONED (A) AND MEAT CAN THEN BE CUBED, SLICED, OR GROUND; BUT REMOVE FELL FIRST (B)

Note: Place the meat through the machine 3 to 5 times to knit and distribute the fat and lean evenly. Then place on special meat patty paper and merchandise as a fresh or frozen item. This muscle can also be mixed with various boneless lamb cuts for lamb patties or lamb burgers.

5. The shank may also be cut up into cubes bone-in and mixed with other lamb stew items and then merchandised as stew, or in a lamb combination form. (See Fig. 8.10.)

6. The shank may also be boned and cut up into stew or may be sliced for cube lamb steaks. It may also be cubed for stews or shish kebabs (see Fig. 8.11A).

Note: It is advisable to remove the fell from the shank before cubing, slicing, or grinding (see Fig. 8.11B).

Necks

Some retailers remove the entire neck at the base of the neck on the lamb carcass, before merchandising the neck into various meat cuts and forms. This method will depend upon how the remainder of the chuck is to be merchandised. If the neck is removed in this fashion, it may become difficult to handle the shoulders when cutting chops. This may result in irregularly sliced chops because the meat cutter may have to cut deeper into the shoulder portion when removing the neck in order to get a wider slice of neck meat. If the neck portion is split down the center of the backbone with the lamb shoulders, the neck will have a small portion of the shoulder

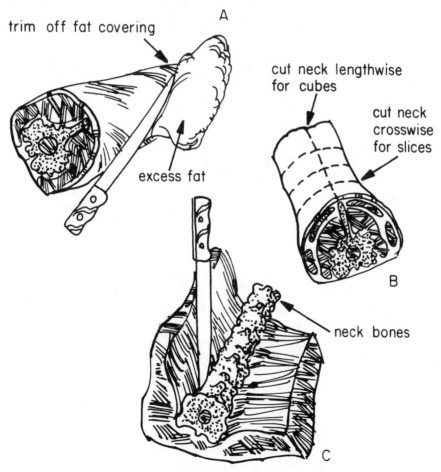

FIG. 8.12. IN MERCHANDISING NECK, FIRST TRIM OFF FAT COVERING (A) AND CUT REMAINDER INTO SLICES OR CUBES (B) OR REMOVE NECK BONES (C) AND MERCHANDISE AS STEW MEAT, CUBE STEAKS, OR GRIND FOR PATTIES

attached to it after the removal of the chops. Retailers generally merchandise this portion as a lamb neck. Any of the following methods may be employed.

1. Remove the fat covering on the whole neck down to the lean. (See Fig. 8.12A.)

   Note: Cut off any discolored meat in the throat region.

2. The whole neck may now be sliced into neck slices or cut into 1- to 1½-in. cubes (bone in) for lamb stew. (See Fig. 8.12B.)

3. The necks may also be boned and cut up into stew meat, or mixed with other trimmings to make cubed lamb steaks, or ground for items such as lamb patties. (See Fig. 8.12C.)

   Note: Some meat cutters dress up the patties with a strip of bacon around the sides of the patty.

4. The neck and shoulder portion may also be cracked through the neck bones to be merchandised whole as a potted item. (See Fig. 8.13).

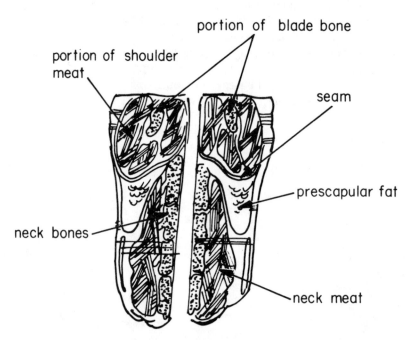

FIG. 8.13. SAW THROUGH NECK BONES AT 1-IN. INTERVALS AND PACKAGE TWO NECKS TO A BOAT FOR A POTTED ITEM

Or meat from the whole neck may be trimmed out and cut into squares for lamb stew meat.

Boning the Shoulder

Meat cutters will employ various methods when boning lamb shoulders. Some may remove the entire foreshank and brisket portion before boning. Others may remove the foreshank, brisket portion, and the neck before boning. The reasons for these variations are numerous. Some meat cutters may not be sufficiently skilled in rolling and tieing whole boneless shoulders, while others may be restricted to following the exact specifications mandated by store merchandising policies and practices. Retailers rarely bone lamb in any form except for cuts which are generally not very popular or attractive to consumers even though these meat items must be utilized or merchandised before spoilage sets in. This practice is not the best form of merchandising lamb specialties. Wholesale meat cutters, especially those engaged in portion control cuts, bone legs and shoulders quite often. Retailers should bone legs and shoulders to increase their sales tonnage of lamb. The following is a suggested method for boning a whole lamb shoulder.

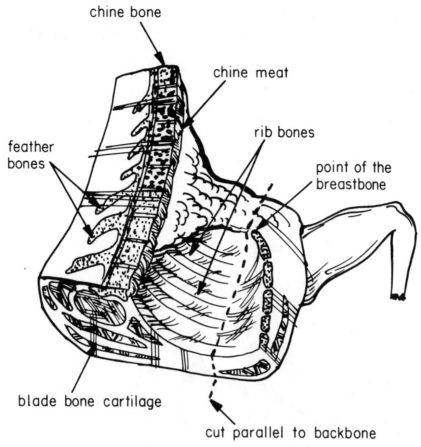

chine bone

chine meat

feather
bones

rib bones

point of the
breastbone

blade bone cartilage

cut parallel to backbone

FIG. 8.14. SAW THROUGH THE RIB BONES

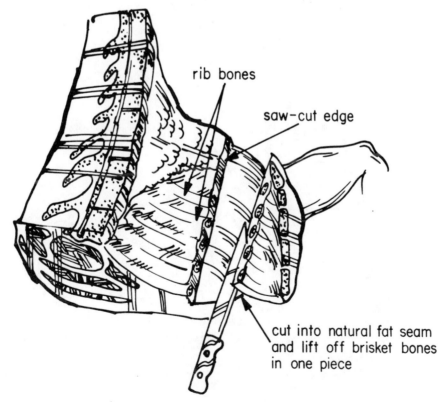

rib bones

saw-cut edge

cut into natural fat seam
and lift off brisket bones
in one piece

FIG. 8.15. CUT OFF BRISKET BONE PORTION FROM SHOULDER

1. Place the shoulder on the bench with the bone side up.
2. Saw through the five rib bones parallel to the backbone, starting at the point of the breast bone (see Fig. 8.14).

   Note: Some meat cutters will omit this step and proceed to step No. 3.

3. Remove the brisket portion at the natural seam (see Fig. 8.15).
4. Loosen and lay back the chine meat past the first rib bone (see Fig. 8.16).
5. Cut along each side of the rib bones to free the finger meat between each rib bone (see Fig. 8.17).

   Note: Some meat cutters will also omit this step in the boning procedure.

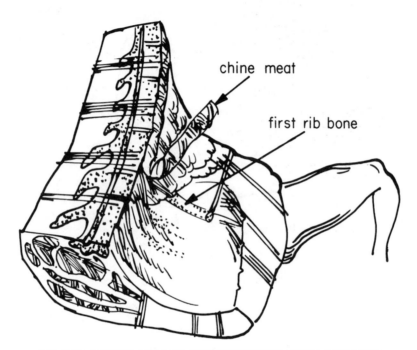

FIG. 8.16. LOOSEN AND LAY BACK CHINE MEAT FROM SHOULDER

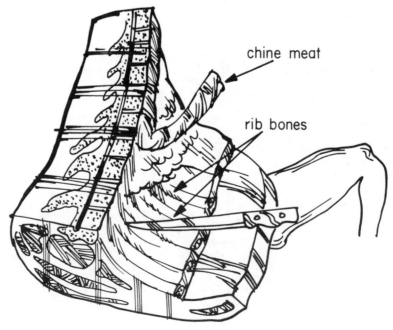

FIG. 8.17. CUT ALONG EACH SIDE OF THE RIB BONES

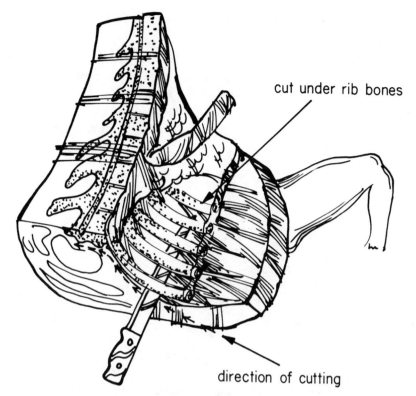

cut under rib bones

direction of cutting

FIG. 8.18. FREE ALL MEAT FROM UNDERSIDE OF RIB BONES

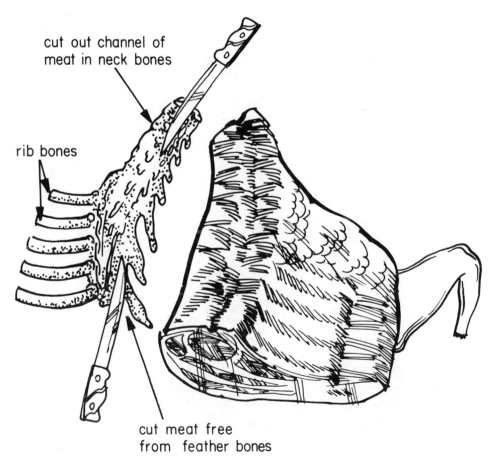

cut out channel of
meat in neck bones

rib bones

cut meat free
from feather bones

FIG. 8.19. CUT RIBS AND BACKBONE FREE IN ONE PIECE

6. Loosen all the meat under each rib bone and the feather bones and lift out the bones in one piece. (See Fig. 8.18 and 8.19.)

   Caution: Keep your free hand in back of the cutting edge of the knife.

   Note: Keep the tip of the knife against the tips of the neck bones removing the channel of meat in the center of the neck bones. (See Fig. 8.19.)

7. Cut through the webbing into the natural fat seam between the shoulders lifting the boneless rib portion away from the shoulder. This will assist you in removing the bones. (See Fig. 8.20.)

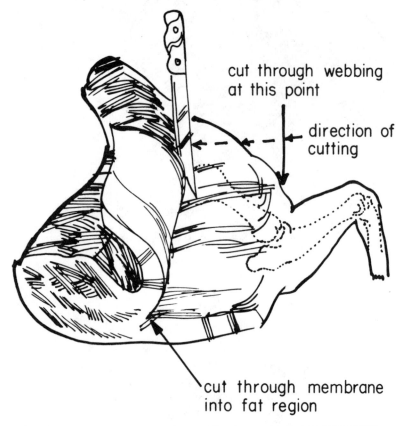

cut through webbing at this point

direction of cutting

cut through membrane into fat region

FIG. 8.20. CUT THROUGH NATURAL SEAM TO LIFT SHOULDER MEAT

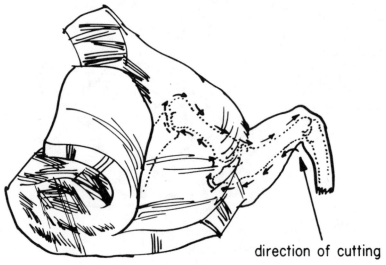

direction of cutting

FIG. 8.21. REMOVE SHANK AND ARM BONES

8. Loosen the meat on both sides of the shank bone by cutting up to the arm bone socket, and through the socket, continuing on to the other side of the bone. Lift the two bones out in one piece. (See Fig. 8.21.)

   Caution: Use only the tip of the boning knife against the bone while cutting through the lean. Some meat cutters prefer to remove these bones one at a time.

9. Cut along the side of the blade bone. Catch the seam at the socket portion of the blade bone and lift the meat from the flat surface of the blade bone. (See Fig. 8.22.)

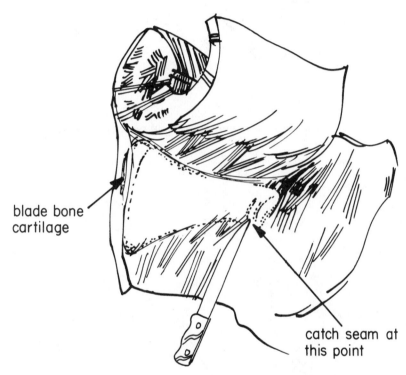

blade bone cartilage

catch seam at this point

FIG. 8.22. CUT MUSCLE FREE FROM FLAT SURFACE OF BLADE BONE

10. Catch the seam by scraping at the exposed end of the ridge bone. (See Fig. 8.23.)

    Note: Use the heel of the knife when scraping.

11. Pull the blade bone free from the shoulder. (See Fig. 8.24.)

Tieing a Boneless Whole Shoulder

Meat cutters will vary the methods of tieing a boneless shoulder. They may remove the neck and shank portions after the shoulder is boned. This method often leads to poor merchandising practice because these cuts should have been removed before boning. The principal purpose in boning the whole shoulder is to merchandise the whole shoulder as a roast. This procedure reduces the cost of the shoulder because the neck and shank are attached to the shoulder and not removed. By merchandising the whole shoulder you are also reducing the trimming time. There are other methods of merchandising the boneless shoulder which retailers will sometimes use. Wholesalers engaged in portion control cuts who supply the hotel, restaurant, and institutional trade, prepare special cuts of lamb from the shoulder. One such cut is called a Saratoga roast. Others are called Saratoga chops. These items are derived from the inside portion of the boneless lamb shoulder which was separated at the natural fat seam. It contains the eye muscle of the shoulder and the

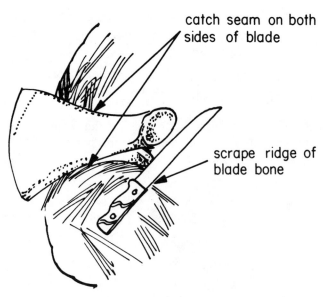

catch seam on both
sides of blade

scrape ridge of
blade bone

FIG. 8.23. FREE MEAT FROM RIDGE OF THE BLADE BONE

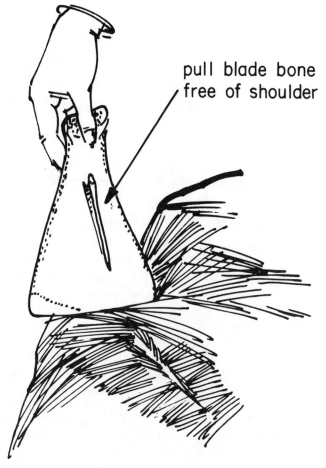

pull blade bone
free of shoulder

FIG. 8.24. LIFT OUT BLADE BONE

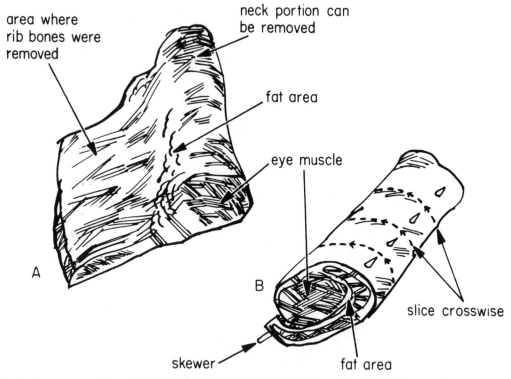

FIG. 8.25. BONELESS INSIDE PORTION OF SHOULDER MAY BE ROLLED, SKEWERED, AND THEN SLICED FOR SARATOGA CHOPS

muscle at the point where the rib bones were removed. This cut is generally rolled and tied, or skewered as a roast. As mentioned above, it is also skewered and sliced into chops called Saratoga chops. (See Fig. 8.25.) The outside portion, which is the clod portion of the shoulder, consists mostly of lean meat. Wholesalers generally use this portion for boneless lamb stew or lamb shish kebab cubes for portion control cuts. Retailers can also use these methods to increase their lamb sales.

Before tieing the boneless shoulder, it is advisable to trim the shoulder of excess fat. The amount of trim will vary with variations in store merchandising practices. It is very important to remove the prescapular fat gland located next to the muscle which is called the chuck tender (see Fig. 8.26). This gland, if left intact, would be very bitter to the taste. It is also important to remember to remove the fat from the

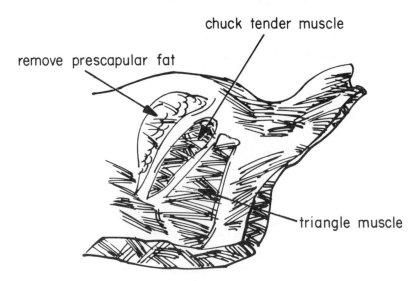

FIG. 8.26. LOCATION OF CHUCK TENDER IN CLOD SECTION OF SHOULDER

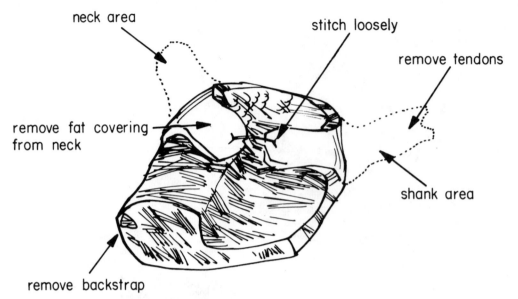

neck area

stitch loosely

remove tendons

remove fat covering
from neck

shank area

remove backstrap

FIG. 8.27. LOOSELY STITCH BONELESS NECK AND BONELESS SHANK TO CENTER OF SHOULDER

neck portion as well as the tendons on the ends of the shank meat (see Fig. 8.27). The following is a suggested method and procedure for tieing the shoulder.

1. Stitch the shank meat and neck meat loosely (see Fig. 8.27).
2. Place a double guide string lengthwise around the shoulder. (See Fig. 8.28.)

   Note: Some retailers will sprinkle the inside cut surfaces with dehydrated egg white powder as a binding agent. This will help to maintain a whole, even slice of meat when the shoulder is cooked and sliced.

3. Place five evenly-spaced cross strings starting at the thick end of the roast (see Fig. 8.28).

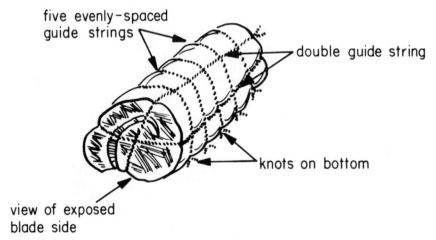

five evenly-spaced
guide strings

double guide string

knots on bottom

view of exposed
blade side

FIG. 8.28. THE BONED WHOLE SHOULDER IS ROLLED AND TIED WITH A
DOUBLE GUIDE STRING AND EVENLY-SPACED CROSS STRINGS

UNIT 9: The Lamb Back

The lamb back contains the hotel rack, the loin, the breast, and the flank. It represents approximately 33% of the carcass. The lamb back is considered to be very tender and retailers rarely have any difficulty in merchandising rib lamb chops and loin lamb chops because of the great consumer demand for these cuts. That portion of the lamb back which may cause some difficulty in merchandising is composed of the breast and the flank. Chain stores and supermarkets rarely cut lamb backs into various types of retail cuts other than chops. It is important to remember that if there is no difficulty in merchandising rib and loin chops, then it becomes very possible to sell more lamb with a variety of cuts from the back. Variety cuts will provide for greater selectivity for the consumer. It is equally important to be flexible in merchandising in order to meet competitive situations. It is better not to rely on one method of cutting because it may limit tonnage sales of lamb. The fundamental reasons underlying the reluctance of managers and supervisors of meat departments to limit the variety of cuts from the lamb back are the cost of labor and the time involved in the processing of these cuts. This is not always the case in every instance with all meat men who process lamb. Other reasons may be attributed to the lack of flexibility and lack of skill and knowledge in the processing of these cuts. The information that follows should be helpful to all, these reasons not withstanding.

Chain stores and supermarkets generally split the lamb back down the center of the backbone. (See Fig. 9.1.) The breast and flank are removed from each side, depending upon store practices. This technique will vary widely from one store to another. It is primarily the selling price of the chops, as well as competitive situations, that will

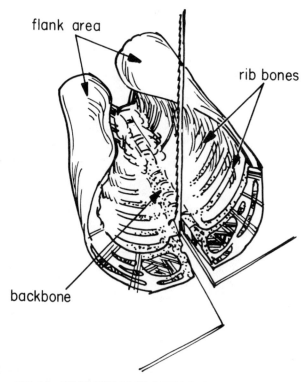

FIG. 9.1. SPLIT THE BACK DOWN THE CENTER OF THE BACKBONE

largely control the amount of flank on the loin and the amount of breast (rib ends) on the rack. Trim is another important factor in competitive situations. Some meat cutters may leave the fell and fat on the chops where others may remove them. There are no set rules and regulations that govern the merchandising of lamb backs except those determined by store merchandising policy. Actually, there are more variations in trimming lamb chops than there are in cutting lamb backs. The following are suggested methods for merchandising the lamb back.

Cutting Rib and Loin Chops

1. Refer back to Fig. 9.1 in splitting the lamb back.
2. Remove the breast and flank by starting at the end of the deckle covering on the blade side and cutting through the rib bones and flank to the outer edge of the flank (see Fig. 9.2).

   Note: This step will vary considerably in accordance with the method and policy adopted by retailers when merchandising the chops. Some meat cutters will measure from the rib eye muscle out toward the breast. This can vary from 2 to 4 in., or even 5 in., from the eye muscle. Again, stress is placed upon the influence of store merchandising practices.

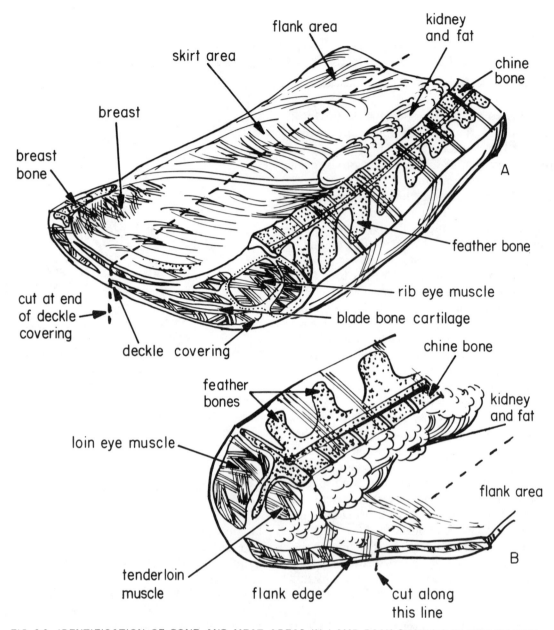

FIG. 9.2. IDENTIFICATION OF BONE AND MEAT AREAS IN LAMB BACK SHOWING WHERE TO CUT
FROM (A) BLADE SIDE OF SPLIT BACK OR (B) LOIN SIDE OF SPLIT BACK

3. Remove the kidney and surrounding fat around the tenderloin muscle (see Fig. 9.2).

   Note: The degree of trim will depend upon store policy.

4. Remove the fell from the outer surface.

   Note: Some retailers may omit this step in accordance with their policies relating to trim. However, it is easier to remove the fell and excess fat before slicing into chops.

5. Cut the chops on the band saw approximately ¾ to 1 in. thick. Start on the loin side first. This will make it easier to handle the rack portion.

6. Remove bone dust and place the chops in various size boats.

   Note: A popular size found in chain stores and supermarkets is one containing four chops to a boat. Package the chops in a flat position so that the customer can see the entire display of the chops.

saw through base
of rib bones

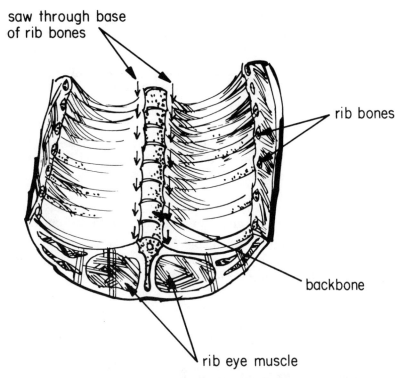

rib bones

backbone

rib eye muscle

FIG. 9.3. INSIDE VIEW OF HOTEL RACK SHOWING WHERE TO SAW
THROUGH BASE OF RIB BONES

remove finger meat
between rib bones

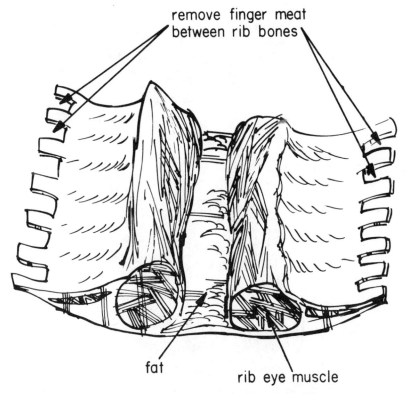

fat

rib eye muscle

FIG. 9.4. "FRENCH" ENDS OF THE RIB BONES

Cutting a Crown Roast From a Hotel Rack (Double)

1. Remove the entire backbone by sawing through at the base of the rib bones on each side of the backbone (see Fig. 9.3).

    Note: Use the tip of the boning knife along the sides of the backbone, being careful not to cut through the fat, and remove the bone in one piece. Some stores may or may not remove the tips of the blade cartilage on the blade side.

2. "French" the ends of the rib bones by removing approximately 1 to 1½ in. from the ends of the rib bones, and the finger meat between the rib bones (see Fig. 9.4).

3. Place two stitches on each end of the rack. Do not secure the knots at this time (see Fig. 9.5A).

4. Shape the racks into a crown; and with the tip of the boning knife, cut at the base between each rib bone. Then secure the knots on the stitches (see Fig. 9.5B).

    Note: The roast is decorated with paper frills on the tip end of each of the rib ends. The center may or may not be stuffed with lean, ground lamb. This is a matter of consumer preference and specification.

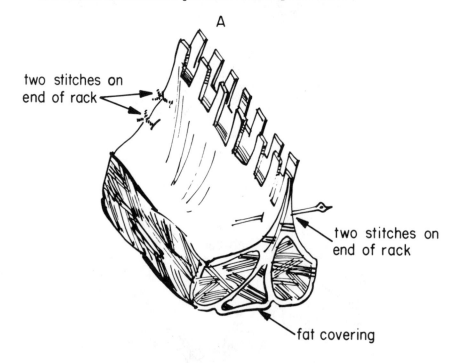

two stitches on end of rack

two stitches on end of rack

fat covering

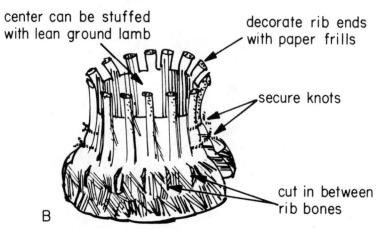

center can be stuffed with lean ground lamb

decorate rib ends with paper frills

secure knots

cut in between rib bones

FIG. 9.5. (A) STITCH HOTEL RACK AT BOTH ENDS AND (B) SHAPE RACK INTO CROWN

Cutting a French Rack Roast From a Hotel Rack

1. Split the hotel rack down the center of the backbone. (See Fig. 9.6A.)
2. "French" the ends of the rib bones by removing approximately 1 to 1½ in. from the ends of the rib bones and the finger meat between the rib bones (see Fig. 9.6B).

    Note: Decorate the ends with paper frills or large pitted olives.

3. Cut through the backbone on the band saw, cutting between each rib bone for easy carving.

    Note: To prepare French rib chops, merely cut the French rack into double thick chops. Remove only one rib end leaving the other end intact (see Fig. 9.6C). Some stores may cut the rack in half for an individual rack rib roast. This is ideal for two people.

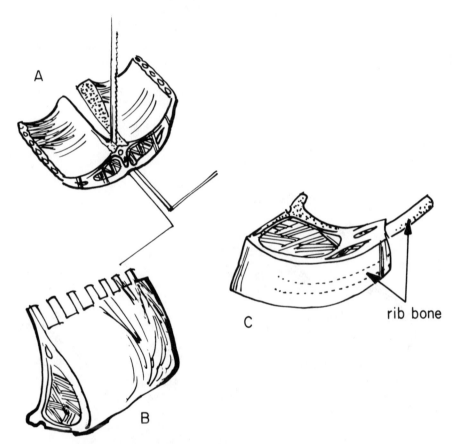

FIG. 9.6. (A) SPLIT HOTEL RACK DOWN THE CENTER OF THE BACKBONE; (B) EACH HALF WILL MAKE A FRENCH RACK ROAST; OR (C) THE RACK MAY BE MADE INTO FRENCH RIB CHOPS

Sawbuck Roast

Follow steps No. 1 through No. 3 above in cutting a French rack. Then interlock the rib ends as shown in Fig. 9.7. Stitch the ends to hold the roast in an upright position.

Boneless Rib Roast

1. Split the hotel rack on the band saw through the center of the backbone.
2. Bone out the rack by starting at the rib ends, cutting close to the rib bones down to the backbone and even with the feather bones (see Fig. 9.8A).

    Note: Remove the back strap, fell, and excess fat.

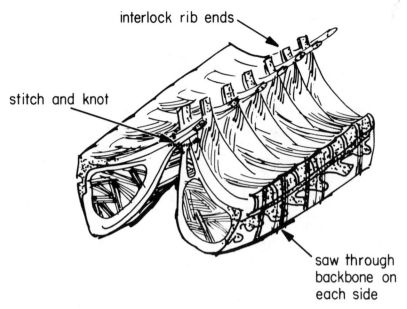

FIG. 9.7. WHEN SPLIT AT BACKBONE, A HOTEL RACK MAY BE MADE INTO A SAWBUCK ROAST BY INTERLOCKING RIB ENDS AND STITCHING THE TWO ENDS TO HOLD ROAST UPRIGHT

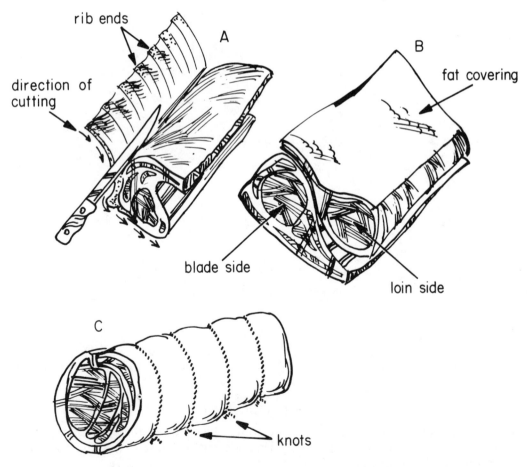

FIG. 9.8. (A) BONE THE SPLIT RACK AS SHOWN, THEN (B) PLACE OPPOSITE ENDS TO EACH OTHER AND (C) ROLL AND TIE TO MAKE A ROLLED, DOUBLE-RACK ROAST

3. Reverse the two boneless racks so that the blade and loin sides show on each side (see Fig. 9.8B).

   Note: This will make the roast even on both ends.

4. Place 4 or 5 evenly-spaced cross strings to properly shape the roast (see Fig. 9.8C).

   Note: This roast may also be sliced into 2-in. slices and merchandised as boneless rib roast chops.

Lamb Loin

Loin lamb chops are the most popular type of lamb chops and are usually the most expensive cuts of lamb. Retailers rarely bone or merchandise roasts from the lamb loin, bone-in or boneless, because of the keen, competitive pricing and merchandising factors characteristic of chain store and supermarket operation. The general feeling among retailers is that lamb loins move quite readily without any further cuts necessary. Although this is true in many cases, there is the important merchandising factor that indicates that by offering consumers greater variety and selectivity, there is an increase in sales volume. This is further supplemented by consistent and repetitive consumer purchases of lamb cuts and a further increase in sales tonnage. The following are suggested methods for merchandising the lamb loin.

Loin Roast (Bone-in)

1. Remove the loin section from the split lamb back by cutting between the 12th and 13th rib bone (see Fig. 9.9).

   Note: Some meat cutters may cut at the end of the 13th rib bone on the rack. This is a matter of store merchandising practice.

2. Remove the kidney and kidney fat. Some meat cutters will leave a ¼-in. covering on the tenderloin.

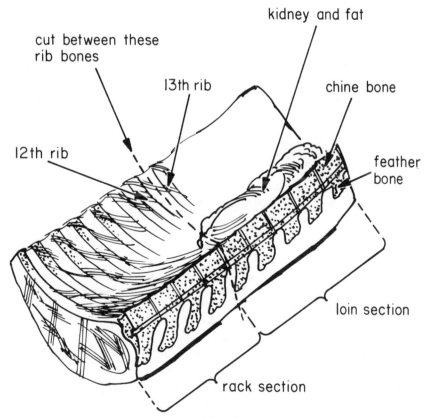

FIG. 9.9. REMOVE LOIN SECTION FROM TRIMMED, SPLIT LAMB BACK

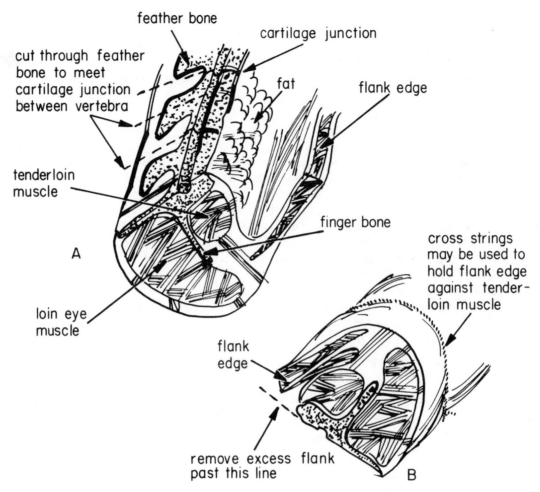

FIG. 9.10. STEPS TO TAKE TO PREPARE A LOIN ROAST WITH BONE IN

3. Cut through the backbone at the cartilage junction between each vertebra (see Fig. 9.10A).

   Note: It is very important to cut at the junction because of the protruding finger bones in the loin. If the backbone is not cut at this junction, when the roast is cooked the consumer may become discouraged if the knife will not cut through the roast because of the bone. Roasts should be easy to carve after they are cooked.

   Note: Do not leave too much of the flank edge on the loin. Level the flank edge with the tenderloin muscle (see Fig. 9.10B).

Loin Roast (Boneless)

Some meat men prepare a roast called a "Lamb Saddle Roast." Although this type of roast is useful for the hotel and restaurant trade, it is not feasible for the retail trade. The processing of this roast consists of boning the double lamb loin in one piece and replacing the bone in its original position and form, and then tieing the double loin. There is no way of cracking the backbone and this would create a carving problem for the consumer. It would be advisable to bone two single lamb loins and tie them together. The following method is suggested for processing of this roast.

1. Follow steps No. 1 and No. 2 in the processing of a bone-in loin roast.
2. Loosen and lay back the tenderloin muscle beyond the ends of the fingerbones (see Fig. 9.11).

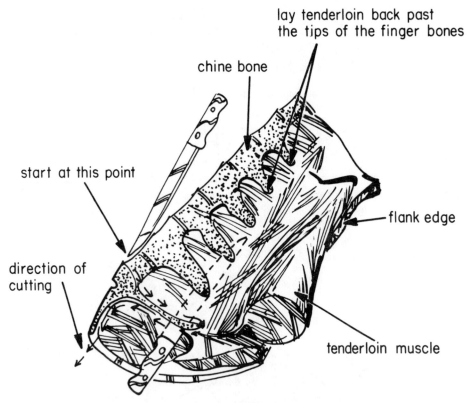

FIG. 9.11. REMOVE BACKBONE IN ONE PIECE

3. Continue to free the meat from the ends of the finger bones down to and through the feather bones (see Fig. 9.11).
4. Reverse the two boneless loins so that the loin and rib side show on each side (see Fig. 9.12).

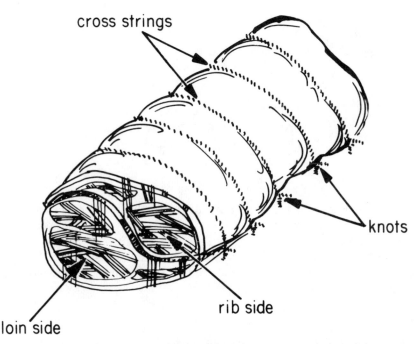

FIG. 9.12. TWO BONELESS LOINS TIED WITH RIB SIDE AND LOIN SIDE SHOWING ON EACH END

Note: It is advisable to sprinkle the inside surfaces with dehydrated egg white powder before tieing. This will prevent separation of the slices after the roast is cooked and while it is being carved.

5. Place cross strings from 1 to 1½ in. apart.

Lamb Breast and Flank

The manner in which the breast and flank were removed from the carcass will often determine the size and shape of the breast and flank. Some meat stores remove the entire rattle which contains the entire breast (breast with brisket portion). (See Fig. 9.13.) When cutting the breast from a lamb bracelet, you will only have the breast minus the flank and brisket portion. The flank region is generally used for lamb trimmings. The membrane is removed as well as some of the

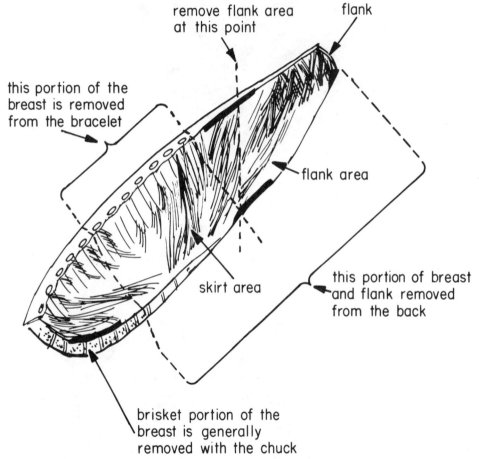

FIG. 9.13. VIEW OF THE ENTIRE BREAST AND FLANK

excess fat. (See Fig. 9.13.) The merchandising of the breast will vary in accordance with the merchandising practices of the store and consumer requests. Many chain stores and supermarkets simply cut breasts of lamb into cubes (bone in) for stew. Some difficulty may arise if the breasts are not selling readily. Therefore, meat cutters should have alternative methods for merchandising the breasts. The following are suggested methods.

Riblets

1. Remove the excess fat from the outside surface of the breast (see Fig. 9.14).
2. Cut between the rib bones and through the breast bone (see Fig. 9.15).

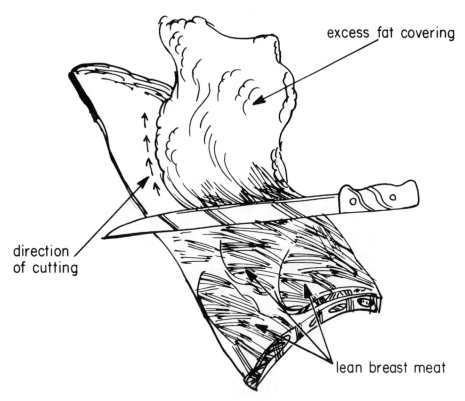

FIG. 9.14. DIRECTION OF CUTTING TO REMOVE EXCESS FAT FROM BREAST

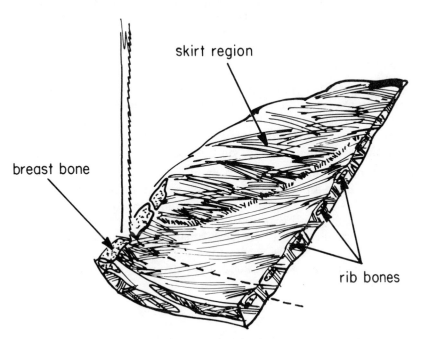

FIG. 9.15. CUT THROUGH BREAST BONE AND BETWEEN RIB BONES

Caution: Keep your fingers clear from the path of the blade.

3. Remove the bone dust and place the riblets in boats with the cut surface facing up (see Fig. 9.16).

   Note: Some stores will label these ribs as barbecue ribs. This is an excellent merchandising item during summer months. Hotel and catering establishments use this item as an appetizer or hot hors d'oeuvre.

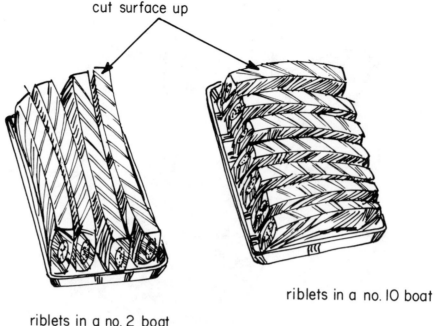

cut surface up

riblets in a no. 2 boat

riblets in a no. 10 boat

FIG. 9.16. PLACE RIBLETS IN BOAT OF SUITABLE SIZE WITH CUT SURFACE
FACING UP

The lamb breast can also be merchandised whole by removing the excess fat and cracking the breast bone. These pieces can be labeled as lamb spare ribs. Some ethnic groups prefer lamb rather than pork.

Lamb Breast with Pocket

1. Remove the excess fat as in step No. 1 above. (Refer back to Fig. 9.14.)
2. Crack the breast bone on the band saw. Do not cut too deep into the breast meat. Merely cut the bone or the variety of stuffings which may later be used may seep or extrude through the cut in the breast bone section (see Fig. 9.15).
3. With a steak knife, open a pocket on the flank end of the breast (see Fig. 9.17).

   Note: Some meat cutters prefer to open a pocket on the rib end side. This may be too large an opening for the consumer to seal after inserting the stuffing. This is a matter of store merchandising practice and also controlled by consumer specification. Where state and local laws permit stuffing, it is advisable to stuff the lamb breast with ground lamb trimmings or sausage mixture. Some stores may slice the stuffed breast and label these slices as stuffed lamb riblets. They can also be labeled as "Scotch Chops" from breast of lamb.

Boning the Breast

1. Loosen and lay back the skirt section of the breast past the rib cartilages (see Fig. 9.18).
2. Cut close to the rib bones, starting at the rib ends, down to the breast bone and rib bone cartilages. Remove the bone in one piece (see Fig. 9.19).

   Note: Do not discard the bones. Cut the bones into squares and merchandise as lamb bones for Scotch broth.

The boneless breast can be used for many items such as ground lamb, lamb cube steaks, rolled breast, lamb patties, or lamb burgers. Meat cutters should be innova-

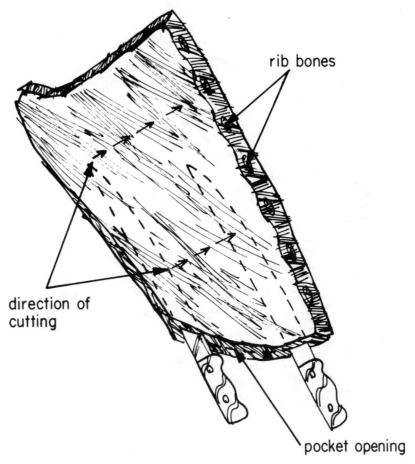

FIG. 9.17. STARTING AT FLANK EDGE, THIS SHOWS DIRECTION OF CUTTING
TO MAKE A POCKET IN BREAST

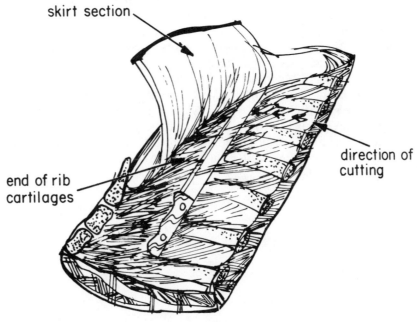

FIG. 9.18. LOOSEN AND LAY BACK SKIRT SECTION

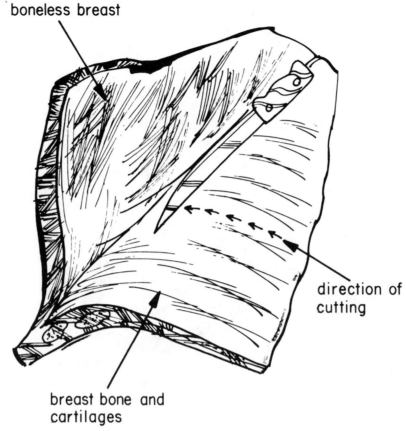

FIG. 9.19. REMOVE RIB BONES AND CARTILAGES

Breast bones and cartilages can be cut into squares and merchandised for Scotch broth.

tive when preparing these cuts. The following are some suggestions for merchandising these lamb specialties:

(1) Narrow cheese strips may be placed in a criss-cross fashion on lamb patties.

(2) Other cuts and specialties may be garnished with pepper rings, sprigs of parsley, sliced onion rings, mushroom buttons, bacon squares, etc.

(3) These and other food garnishes can be prepared in advance and placed on the lamb cuts and specialties just before they are packaged and placed in the fresh meat display case. They may also garnish meat packages that will be placed in the freezer.

Some of these meat items, with or without the garnish, may not move or merchandise as readily as anticipated. It is advisable to change merchandising methods and adopt new innovations to attract the consumer. Very often, colorful pictures of lamb specialty dishes may create consumer interest. Whatever the method or technique, effective merchandising will require a degree of experiment, challenge, and innovation to increase sales.

Section III: VEAL

UNIT 10: Veal Classifications, Weights, and Cuts

Veal and calf carcasses are derived from the young of the bovine species (cattle). The flesh obtained from these animals is called veal whether they are veal or calf carcasses. Generally, all retail cuts from these carcasses are labeled with the introductory term "veal." There are some exceptions within the offal products. These products are the liver, hearts, sweet-breads, tongues, and brains. These offal specialties are usually labeled with the preface word "calf."

The factors affecting the classes of veal are the age, the weight, and the feed. The bulk of the veal carcasses is obtained from the dairy industry because male calves are of no value to the dairy industry. The principal products of this industry are milk and milk products. At present, it is interesting to note that the leading States of the country in the production of milk and milk products are New York and Wisconsin. The bulk of veal is, therefore, largely derived from these two States. The source of calf carcasses is largely derived from the beef industry.

General Processing and Marketing of Veal

The meat derived from the very young of the bovine species (cattle family) is fine-grained and the color of the lean will vary from a light pink to a dark, grayish pink. The bones are very soft and red. Some of the quality factors of vealers are usually indicated by the nature of the kidney fat and the thin covering of fat in higher grades of veal. Wholesalers in the New York Metropolitan area rarely purchase graded veal because of the added cost. The veal is usually purchased in carcass form with the hide on in order to protect the carcass and to prevent shrinkage. Veal has a high percentage of moisture. Its moisture content is higher than most other forms of livestock. Wholesalers will generally purchase veal by the carload in mixed weights with the hide on (ungraded). Retailers usually rely upon the knowledge of the wholesaler when they purchase veal from them. It is because veal and calf carcasses have small amounts of fat as compared with the various grades of beef that conformation becomes difficult in the grading of veal. Quality is the most important factor in grading veal and conformation varies widely because of the variations in

youth and maturity. Vealers are generally milk fed only.

Calf carcasses are derived from the young of the bovine species in the age period between the veal and the yearling (9 months) beef class. The meat is coarser-grained and the color will vary from brown, reddish-tan to a light or deep cherry red, depending upon the feed. These animals have generally been fed on grain, hay, and grasses. The better grades of calves have heavier covering of fat than the lower grades of calves.

Veal is the most expensive type of meat in the wholesale market and equally so in the retail stores. This is largely due to the high demand and often inadequate supply of veal. The leading center of veal merchandising and volume of sales is located in the New York Metropolitan area. This is primarily due to the consumer demands of various ethnic groups who prefer veal for many menu items and food specialties related to the specific group. Veal is also an important food in diet-controlled menus. This applies particularly to special diets medically specified because of the blandness of veal meat.

It must be emphasized that veal contains the highest percentage of moisture as compared with other meats derived from the bovine species. Because of this fact, it is one of the more difficult types of meat to process into various retail cuts. Lack of skill and knowledge in processing and merchandising veal may be the principal cause for chain stores and supermarkets to have a minimal display in their meat cases and a small variety of veal cuts. Lack of knowledge of the bone structure of veal, the meat composition and structure, the seaming, cubing, slicing, and processing of veal into retail cuts can readily be eliminated with careful training and practical experience.

Classifications

Veal is generally classified by age, weight, and feed. The U.S. Department of Agriculture lists two classes of veal: veal and calves. However, veal wholesalers have increased the number of classifications to four categories. Following is a brief explanation of the characteristics of each.

1. **Baby Veal**—Generally referred to as "Bob

Veal." Age covers the span of 2-3 days to 1 month. Weight will vary from 20 to 60 lb. The bulk of these carcasses are male calves from the dairy industry.

2. **Vealers**—The age of vealers will vary from 1 to 3 months. Weight will vary from 80 to 150 lb. They are generally raised primarily on milk. The bulk of these carcasses are derived from the dairy industry.

3. **Calves**—The age of calves will vary from 3 to 8 months. Weight will vary from 125 to 300 lb. They have subsisted partially, or entirely, on feeds other than milk. Their physical characteristics are in the process of change from the veal stage to the beef stage. These carcasses are generally derived from the beef industry.

4. **Nature Veal**—The age is approximately 16 weeks. Weight will vary from 180 to 240 lb. They are developed with a controlled, scientific diet. They have no, or very limited, activity to prevent excessive muscular development. This controlled regimen (diet and activity) produces a white, pinkish color to the lean. This is the most expensive type of veal in the wholesale market.

Grades

There are six grades of veal or calf carcasses. These are Prime, Choice, Good, Standard, Utility, and Cull. The USDA places the grade designation in a stamped shield. In addition to the grade stamp, the word "veal" or "calf" is also stamped directly under the shield. It is important to remember that the basic difference between veal and calf is maturity and color of the lean.

Primal and Subprimal Cuts

The breakdown of veal carcasses will vary widely from one region of the country to another. Veal is generally cut up into primal and subprimal cuts, somewhat similar to lamb. One area of the country that is an exception to this practice is Northeastern United States. This is fundamentally due to the various ethnic groups that make up the population of this section of the country and the special consumer demands for boneless, retail cuts of veal. Wholesale and retail cuts are somewhat similar. Variations will depend upon the wholesalers' processing practices. The most economical method of purchasing veal is in carcass form. This method will ordinarily save the retailer approximately 12% of the cost. However, this practice may not be feasible for all retailers because various groups request more retail cuts from only certain parts of the carcass rather than the whole carcass. This makes it difficult for the retailer to merchandise those cuts of veal which are not as popular nor in as great demand. With some practice and skill, this situation can be overcome. Many retailers generally purchase additional primal and subprimal cuts of veal, depending upon their merchandising practices and consumer demand. The following are some methods which packers and wholesale veal houses will use to break down veal carcasses for retailers.

Veal Side

A veal side is ½ of a carcass which is cut and split down the center of the backbone. It contains all the meat from the hind shank down to the foreshank bone.

Veal Hindsaddle

There are two methods employed by wholesalers in the processing of hindsaddles. These are as follows:

1. The veal carcass is cut between the 12th and 13th rib bones. The hindsaddle is that portion composed of the legs and the loin. The 13th rib bone is in the loin section of the hindsaddle. (See Fig. 10.1.)

2. In the New York Metropolitan area, a veal hindsaddle is generally processed by cutting between the 11th and 12th rib bones. The hindsaddle is composed of the legs and the loin. The 12th and 13th rib bones are left in the loin section of the hindsaddle. The hindsaddle will represent approximately 51% of the carcass. Wholesalers leave an extra rib on the hindsaddle because of the price factor. Hindsaddles cost approximately 50¢ per lb higher than foresaddles. (See Fig. 10.1.)

Veal Foresaddle

A veal foresaddle is that portion of the carcass remaining after the removal of the hindsaddle from the total veal carcass. (See Fig. 10.1.)

Veal Loin

A veal loin is processed from the carcass by cutting at the end of the pelvic bone (hip end) and cutting between the 12th and 13th rib bone. The 13th rib bone and flank are attached to the loin. (See Fig. 10.2.)

In the New York Metropolitan area, a veal loin is removed from the carcass by cutting approximately 1 in. below the end of the pelvic bone (hip end) and then cutting between the 11th and 12th rib bones. The 12th and 13th rib bones and flank are attached to the loin. A pair of veal legs will usually cost more than hindsaddles of veal. (See Fig. 10.2.)

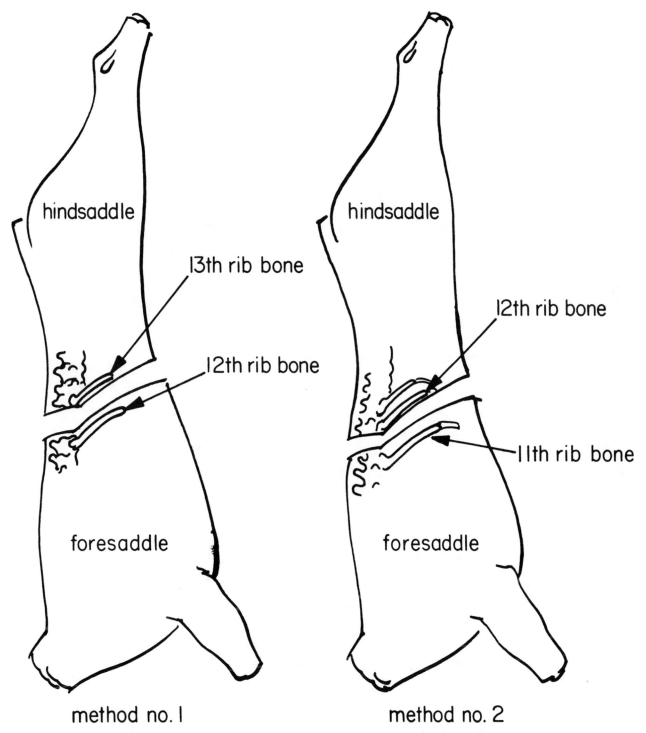

FIG. 10.1. THERE ARE TWO METHODS OF SEPARATING THE HINDSADDLE FROM THE FORESADDLE: (1) BETWEEN THE 12TH AND 13TH RIB BONES AND (2) BETWEEN THE 11TH AND 12TH RIB BONES

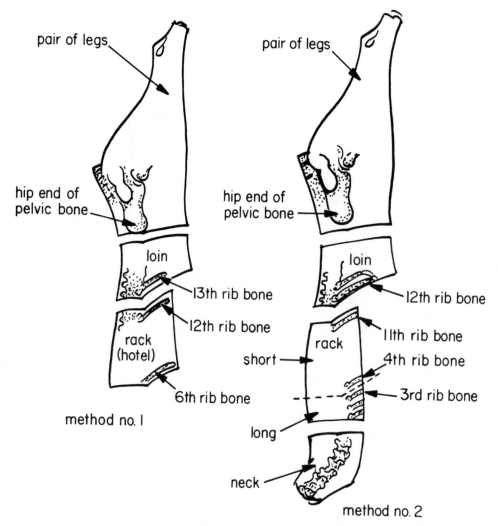

FIG. 10.2. HOW TO CUT A LOIN AND A RACK FROM THE CARCASS FOLLOWING METHOD
NO. 1 OR METHOD NO. 2

Veal Rack

There are three methods which wholesalers may employ in removing the rack from the carcass. In method No. 1, the blade bone cartilage is left intact.   In methods No. 2 and No. 3, the veal shoulder is lifted from the foresaddle. (See Fig. 10.2.)

1. A cut is made between the 12th and 13th rib bones and between the 5th and 6th rib bones. Another cut is made across the rib bones parallel to the backbone, approximately 4 in. from the eye muscle.   This is also referred to as a hotel rack (double). (See Fig. 10.2.)

2. A cut is made between the 11th and 12th rib bones.   Another cut is made across all of the 11 rib bones parallel to the backbone, approximately 2 in. from the rib eye muscle.   Another cut is made at the end of the first rib bone perpendicular to the backbone.   Wholesalers refer to this type of rack as a long veal rack.   It will contain all 11 rib bones in the rack. (See Fig. 10.2.)

3. Follow the same steps as in No. 2, except that the rack is removed by cutting between the 11th and 12th rib bones and cutting between the 3rd and 4th rib bones.   Wholesalers refer to this type of rack as a short veal rack.   It will contain 8 rib bones. (See Fig. 10.2.)

Veal Legs (Pair)

Veal legs are processed from the veal carcass by cutting at the end of the pelvic bone (hip end). Many wholesalers cut below the end of the hip bone because the price for veal legs are higher than that of veal hindsaddles.   This is the most popular type of wholesale cut purchased by retailers.

Veal Bracelet (Double)

A veal bracelet is processed from the veal fore-saddle by cutting between the 5th and 6th rib bones and through the backbone and breastbone. It contains the veal rack and a portion of the breast all in one piece. (See Fig. 10.3A.)

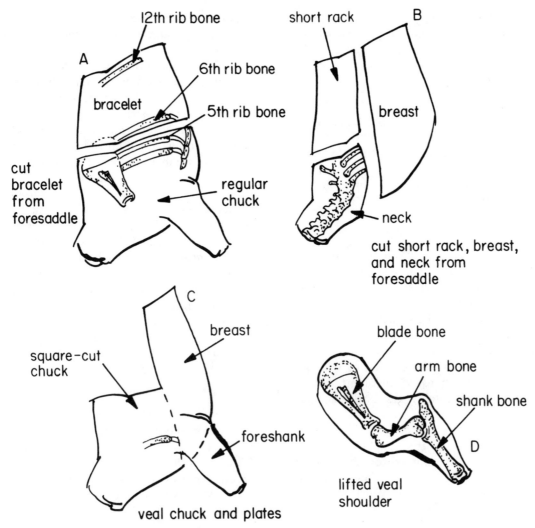

FIG. 10.3. VEAL CUTS FROM THE FORESADDLE: (A) BRACELET AND REGULAR CHUCK; (B) SHORT RACK, BREAST, AND NECK; (C) CHUCK AND PLATE; (D) LIFTED SHOULDER

Veal Chucks and Plates (Double)

Veal chucks and plates are that portion of the foresaddle remaining after removal of the hotel veal rack. (See Fig. 10.3B.)

Veal Chuck, Regular (Double)

The regular veal chuck is that portion of the foresaddle remaining after the removal of the veal bracelet. It is similar to the full beef chuck (cross-cut beef chuck). (See Fig. 10.3A.)

Veal Square-Cut Chucks

A veal square-cut chuck is that portion of the regular veal chuck remaining after removal of the brisket and foreshank by cutting through the cartilaginous juncture of the first rib bone. It will resemble a square-cut chuck of lamb. (See Fig. 10.3B.)

Veal Breast

The breast is that portion of the forequarter remaining after removal of the rack, square-cut chuck, and the foreshank. Some breasts will be larger than others, depending upon how many inches away from the rib eye muscle that the racks were removed. (See Fig. 10.3C.)

Veal Foreshank

A veal foreshank is processed from the veal foresaddle by cutting approximately 1 to 2 in. from the elbow portion of the foreshank bone and cutting through the web muscle into the natural seam between the brisket and the foreshank. (See Fig. 10.3B.)

Veal Neck

A veal neck is that part of the foresaddle after removal of the short or long rack, the breast, and the lifted shoulder. It may contain 3 rib bones, or no rib bones at all, depending upon how the rack was removed from the foresaddle. (See Fig. 10.3C.)

Lifted Veal Shoulder

A lifted veal shoulder is processed from the foresaddle by cutting through the web muscle into the natural seam between the brisket and foreshank, down to and around the end of the blade bone cartilage. It will contain the shank, arm, and blade bone. It is somewhat similar to the long beef shoulder. (See Fig. 10.3D.)

Boneless Veal Cuts

Shoulder Clods.—Veal shoulder clods are generally processed from the lifted veal shoulder. All the bones are removed and some wholesalers will also remove the shank meat. This is a matter of merchandising practice followed by the individual wholesaler. Wholesalers will fabricate boneless or bone-in veal cuts in accordance with the retailers' specifications as long as the retailer is willing to pay the price. Variations of different cuts are widely accepted in wholesale markets in accordance with specifications.

Veal Fillets (Rib Eye Muscle).—Veal fillets are generally processed from the long or short veal rack. All the bones are removed together with the flank edge. The back strap is also removed. Generally, these veal fillets are only found in the markets of the Northeastern part of the country. Retailers purchase these fillets to prepare roasts and cutlets.

T.B.S. (Tops, Bottoms, and Sirloins).—Veal tops, bottoms, and sirloins are cuts processed from the veal leg. All the bones are removed and they are generally composed of the top round, bottom round, and sirloin muscles. The bulk of these muscles are usually removed from vealers. Retailers purchase them in boxes of 25-lb weights and slice them into Italian-style cutlets.

Veal Cutlets.—Cutlets are prepared from the boneless veal leg. Wholesalers pack them fresh in 25-lb weights. They are sliced into thin slices from ⅛ in. to ¼ in. in thickness. Generally, all of the thin membrane from each of the muscles of the leg is removed before slicing. The bulk of this processed meat is usually purchased by hotels, restaurants, and institutions. Some retailers may purchase prepared cutlets to save labor costs and time, even though it then becomes a high cost type of wholesale cut.

Suggested References

For further information regarding institutional types of veal cuts, write to the National Association of Meat Purveyors, 120 S. Riverside Plaza, Chicago, Illinois 60606 and request the following pamphlets: *Meat Buyer's Guide to Portion Control Meat Cuts*, and *Meat Buyer's Guide to Standardized Meat Cuts*.

UNIT 11: Veal Hindsaddles

The hindsaddle of veal represents approximately 51% of the carcass when split between the 11th and 12th rib bones. The hindsaddle is also composed of the two major wholesale cuts known as the legs and loin. These cuts can be purchased from wholesalers either separately, or together as one unit, and are called veal hindsaddles. This unit will treat and explain all the retail cuts derived from the hindsaddle. Hindsaddles cost approximately 50¢ per lb more than foresaddles because the ratio of meat to bone is higher in hindsaddles than in foresaddles. Retailers generally purchase veal legs in pairs more so than hindsaddles because of the popularity of the cuts processed from the legs. Because of the high cost of veal to the retailers, it is essential that retail meat men acquire the skill and knowledge related to the processing and merchandising of veal. Veal, because of its lack of fat covering (external and internal), will not stand up as well as beef and lamb while being processed and merchandised. It tends to lose its bloom much faster than any other type of meat.

As indicated in Unit 10, chainstores and supermarkets generally have a limited amount of veal cuts in their display cases. This may be attributed to the low supply of veal available and the resulting high cost because of the scarcity of the meat. It may also be due to lack of skill and knowledge of processing and merchandising techniques. To begin, let us examine the bone structure of the hindsaddle (see Fig. 11.1). It consists of the hind shank bone, leg bone, pelvic bone, knee cap, tail bone, backbone (feather, chine, and finger bones), and the 13th rib bone. The loin is removed from the hindsaddle by cutting at the end of the pelvic bone (hip end). The muscle structure of veal is the same as it is in beef, with the difference being smaller in size. The retail cuts derived from the hindsaddle will vary from store to store.

THE VEAL LOIN

Refer to Fig. 11.1 to familiarize yourself with the bone structure of the loin. The loin contains the backbone (feather, finger, and chine bones) and the 13th rib or the 12th and 13th rib bones, depending upon how it was removed from the carcass. The muscle structure of the lion consists of the loin eye muscle, tenderloin muscle, and the flank edge (tail). The length of the flank edge attached to the loin eye muscle will vary from store to store. Some stores will leave a flank edge (tail) of 2, 3, or 4 in. from the loin eye muscle. This is a matter of store merchandising practice. Before cutting the loin into retail cuts, the kidney knobs, hanging tender, and veal flank should be removed (see Fig. 11.2). The methods used in trimming the loin will vary. Some meat cutters will also remove the rib bones. The amount of internal fat will vary from store to store. The trimmed loin is then cut through the center of the backbone (see Fig. 11.3).

Cutting Loin Chops

1. Place the loin on the movable carriage with the backbone facing the blade.

   Note: It is advisable to have apprentice meat cutters start at the loin side first to make handling at the end of the rib side easier (see Fig. 11.4).

2. Cut the chops approximately ½ to ¾ in. in thickness.

   Caution: Guide chops through the blade with your left hand. Do not force or pull the chops through the blade.

3. Remove the bone dust and place chops in various size boats for the consumer to make a preferred choice. Keep chops in a flat position in the boats so that the customer can see the entire display in the package.

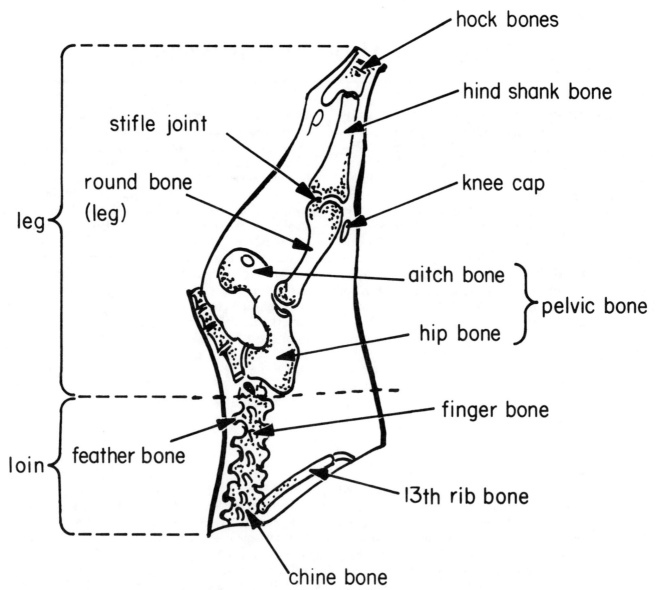

FIG. 11.1. BONE STRUCTURE OF THE HINDSADDLE

Cutting Kidney Chops

Follow the same steps as in cutting loin chops given above. However, it is important that the meat cutter be aware of the fact that the veal kidney is left intact in most cases. Some meat cutters will trim some of the excess fat around the kidney before slicing. Others may remove the entire kidney, trim the kidney, slice the kidney separately, and then replace the kidney slice between the flank edge and loin eye muscle of the chop. The method used is generally determined by the amount of kidney fat on the loin. Good grades of veal will have a large kidney knob while poorer grades will have a small amount of kidney fat.

Loin Roast (Bone-in)

A veal loin roast is somewhat similar to that of lamb, except that it is larger in size. Some meat cutters prefer to remove the last rib bones in the loin and merchandise them as chops. This is a matter of individual store practice.

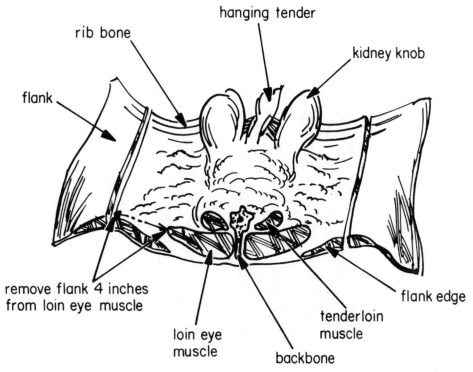

FIG. 11.2. INSIDE VIEW OF THE DOUBLE LOIN

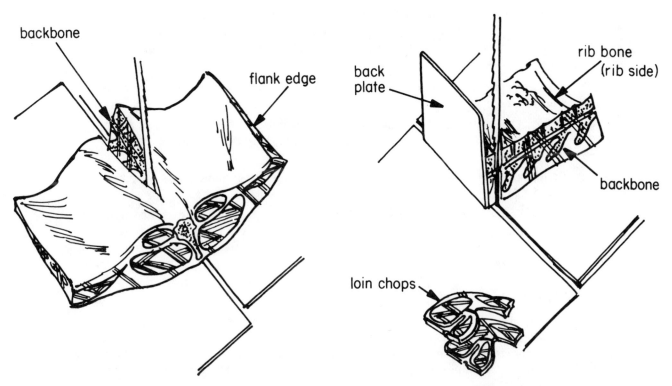

FIG. 11.3. CUT THROUGH CENTER OF BACKBONE OF DOUBLE LOIN

FIG. 11.4. WITH BACKBONE TOWARDS CUTTING BLADE, CUT LOIN CHOPS

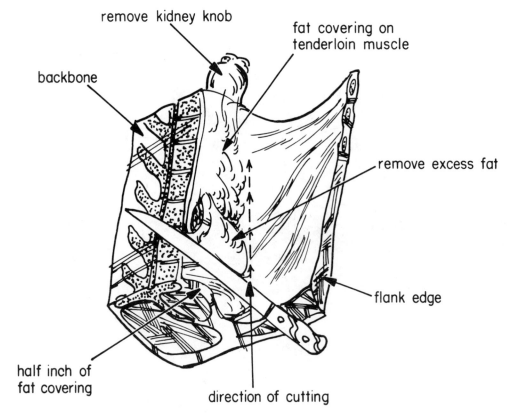

FIG. 11.5. LOCATION OF KIDNEY AND FAT COVERING ON TENDERLOIN MUSCLE WHICH SHOULD BE REMOVED FOLLOWING DIRECTION OF CUTTING AS SHOWN

1. Remove the kidney and fat around the tenderloin muscle (see Fig. 11.5).

    Note: Leave ¼ to ½ in. of fat covering on the tenderloin muscle. A good portion of the fat will melt during the cooking process and make for a more flavorful roast.

2. Cut through the backbone at the cartilage junction between each vertebra (see Fig. 11.6).

    Note: This will make it easier for the consumer to carve the roast after it is cooked because of the protruding finger bone extending between the tenderloin muscle and the loin eye muscle.

3. String tie the roast between each cut to hold the flank edge in place (see Fig. 11.7).

    Note: Some stores will omit this step and package the roast without tieing the flank edge to the roast. Some may remove the entire flank edge or cut the flank edge short. Once again, this is a matter of store merchandising practice.

Loin Roast (Boneless)

1. Loosen and lay back the tenderloin muscle past the ends of the exposed finger bones (see Fig. 11.8).
2. Continue to cut along the opposite side of the finger bones down to and along the side of the bone to free the bone in one piece (see Fig. 11.9).

    Note: Meat cutters may or may not cut around each finger bone. Some may use the scalping method to save time. This is determined by store merchandising practices.

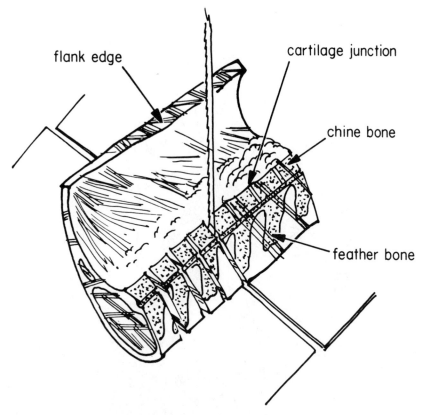

FIG. 11.6. FOR A BONE-IN LOIN ROAST, MAKE SAW CUTS AT CARTILAGE JUNCTIONS ON CHINE BONE

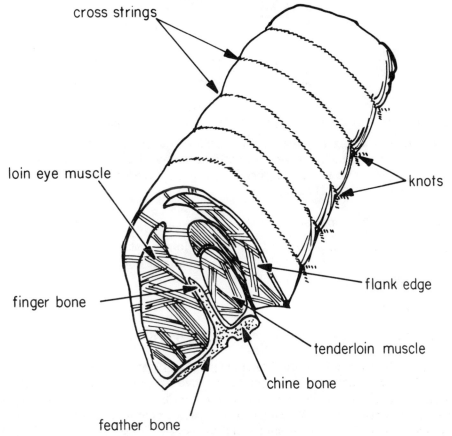

FIG. 11.7. SECURE FLANK EDGE TO ROAST WITH EVENLY-SPACED CROSS STRINGS

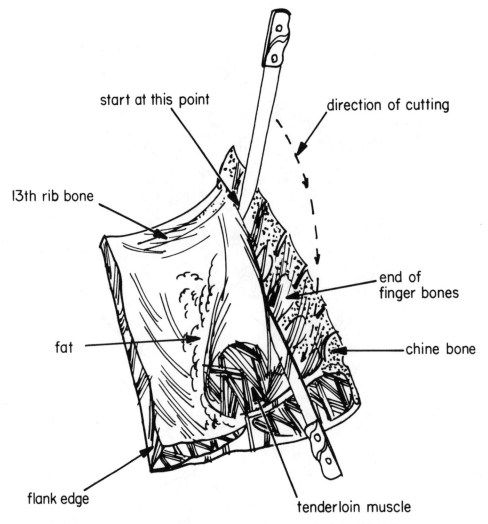

FIG. 11.8. LOOSEN AND LAY BACK TENDERLOIN MUSCLE

3. Place or space cross strings approximately 1 to 1½ in. apart (see Fig. 11.10A).

   Note: Before tieing the roast some retailers may remove the tenderloin muscle and merchandise it separately. They may also tie two boneless roasts together. This roast may then be cut in half crosswise to make two boneless roasts (see Fig. 11.10B).

Loin Kidney Roast (Boneless)

Follow the same procedure as for boneless loin roast given above. Place 1 or 2 veal kidneys (trimmed of fat) between the flank edge and the tenderloin muscle before tieing the roast (see Fig. 11.11).

Stuffed Loin Chops

To process stuffed veal loin chops from the veal loin, follow the same procedure as in cutting loin chops except chops should be cut 1 to 1½ in. thick. Place a pocket in the loin eye muscle for stuffing (see Fig. 11.12). Very often in some chain stores and supermarkets, veal loins may not move as readily as desired. If this occurs it becomes necessary to make changes in merchandising methods. If the loins do not sell as well as chops or roasts, they can be boned, separated into three muscles (loin eye, tenderloin, and flank edge) and sliced into cutlets (see Fig. 11.13). The method

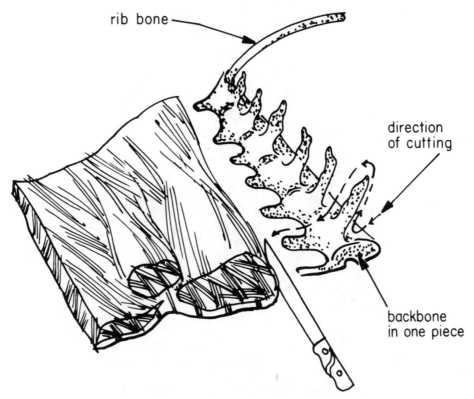

FIG. 11.9. BACKBONE AND RIB ARE THEN REMOVED IN ONE PIECE LEAVING BONED
LOIN IN ONE PIECE

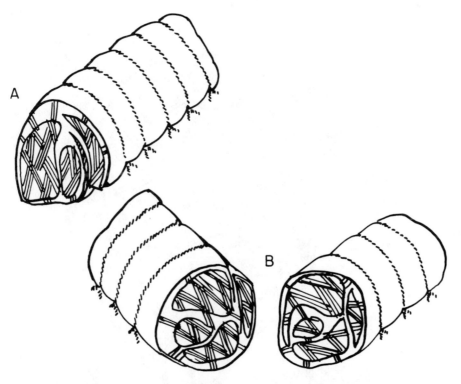

FIG. 11.10. FLANK EDGE OF BONED SINGLE LOIN IS THEN SECURED TO ROAST WITH
EVENLY-SPACED CROSS STRINGS (A) OR, A DOUBLE LOIN (B) MAY BE TIED TO-
GETHER THEN CUT IN HALF CROSSWISE MAKING TWO ROASTS

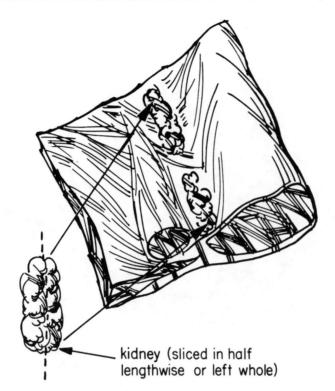

kidney (sliced in half
lengthwise or left whole)

FIG. 11.11. SOMETIMES THE KIDNEY—LEFT WHOLE OR
SLICED IN HALF LENGTHWISE—IS ROLLED IN WITH THE
BONELESS LOIN FOR ROASTING

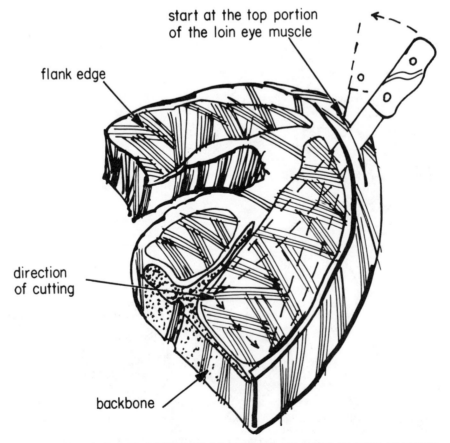

start at the top portion
of the loin eye muscle

flank edge

direction
of cutting

backbone

FIG. 11.12. THIS SHOWS DIRECTION OF CUTTING TO MAKE POCKET IN THICK
LOIN CHOP FOR STUFFING

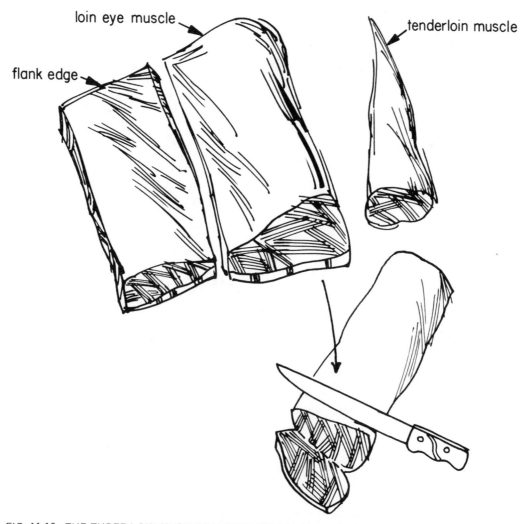

loin eye muscle

tenderloin muscle

flank edge

FIG. 11.13. THE THREE LOIN MUSCLES MAY BE SEPARATED AND SLICED FOR CUTLETS AS SHOWN

or technique will vary depending upon the meat cutter and store merchandising practice. This may not be feasible for all retailers because of the time factor and the added labor cost. However, the final decision is usually made on the basis of a seasoned merchandising background and with an equal experience in meat cutting.

THE VEAL LEG

Retail cuts derived from the leg are the most popular types of cuts merchandised in retail stores. They include the rump of veal roast (bone in and boneless), leg of veal roast, veal steaks, and veal cutlets. These are the principal meat items processed from the leg. Other types of retail cuts, not quite as popular, will also be presented in this unit.

The following are suggested methods for merchandising the veal leg.

The veal rump contains a high percentage of bone. Refer back to Fig. 11.1 and examine the bone structure of the leg. The rump has the entire pelvic bone, tail, backbone, and the ball portion of the leg bone. The rump, being a bony cut, usually is boned out entirely. It may then be merchandised in a manner that is best suited to store policy.

Cutting the Rump From the Leg

1. Place the leg on the band saw with the aitch bone facing up.
2. Cut through the leg approximately 1 in. from the knob of the aitch bone and parallel with the bone.

   Caution: Keep your fingers and hands clear of the path of the blade (see Fig. 11.14).

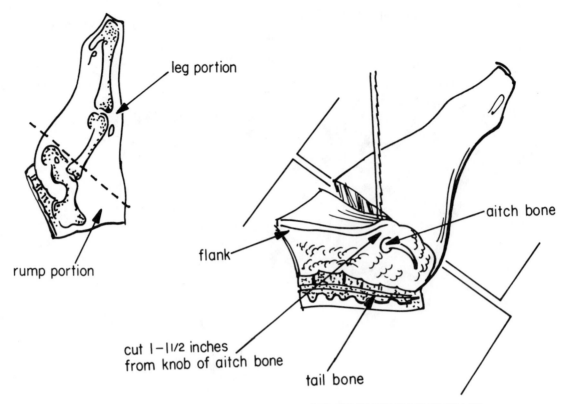

leg portion

rump portion

flank

aitch bone

cut 1–11/2 inches
from knob of aitch bone

tail bone

FIG. 11.14. ANGLE AND LOCATION OF CUT TO SEPARATE RUMP FROM LEG

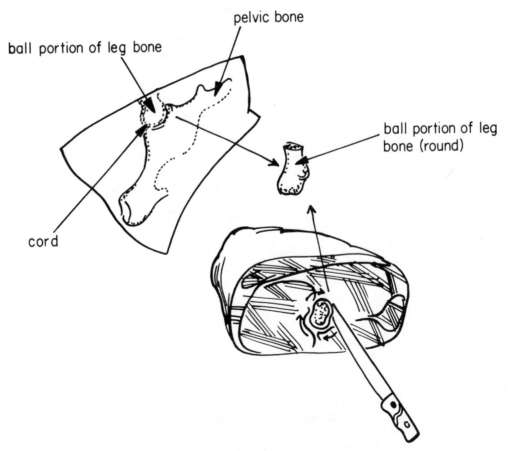

pelvic bone

ball portion of leg bone

ball portion of leg
bone (round)

cord

FIG. 11.15. SHOWS BONE STRUCTURE (ABOVE) OF RUMP AND LOCATION OF BALL PORTION
OF ROUND LEG BONE WHICH SHOULD BE REMOVED (BELOW) AS SHOWN

Note: Some meat cutters may cut closer to the aitch bone. This procedure will cause the rump to have an even bonier appearance which may discourage customers from purchasing this cut.

3. Remove the ball portion of the leg bone from the socket portion of the pelvic bone (see Fig. 11.15).
4. Saw through the backbone and tail bone to make carving easier after cooking.

   Note: If rumps are cut from large legs, it is advisable to cut the rumps in half and make two roasts (see Fig. 11.16).

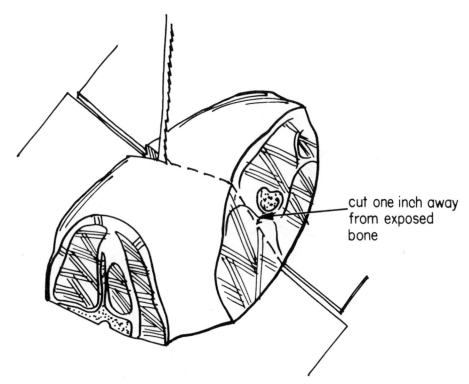

cut one inch away
from exposed
bone

FIG. 11.16. LOCATION OF CUT TO SEPARATE RUMP INTO TWO ROASTS

Cutting Rump Steaks From the Rump

1. Place the veal rump on the band saw with the backbone facing the blade and the loin side against the back plate.
2. Slice the rump steaks approximately 3/4-in. thick (see Fig. 11.17).

   Note: It is advisable to slice steaks only as far as the aitch bone socket. The remainder can then be merchandised as a rump roast or boned for veal cutlets. Some meat cutters will trim these rump steaks by cutting off a portion of the bone. This is a matter determined by store veal trimming practices.

Cutting Steaks From the Leg

Before cutting the steaks, the rump is removed from the leg. The thickness of the steak will vary from store to store.

1. Place the leg on the band saw with the cut surface facing the back plate (see Fig. 11.18).
2. Saw through the leg and leg bone at the desired thickness guiding the steak through the blade with your free hand.

   Caution: Keep your fingers clear from the path of the blade.

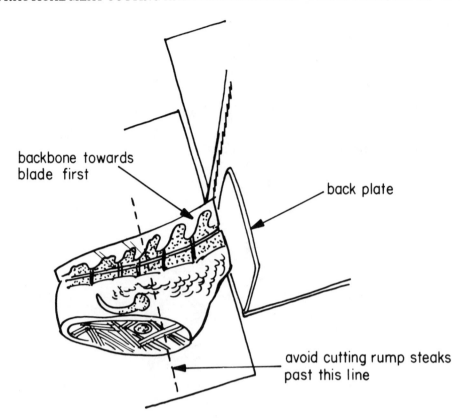

backbone towards
blade first

back plate

avoid cutting rump steaks
past this line

FIG. 11.17. VEAL STEAKS MAY BE CUT FROM A PORTION OF THE RUMP

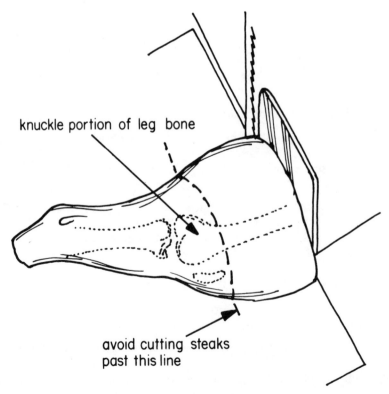

knuckle portion of leg bone

avoid cutting steaks
past this line

FIG. 11.18. UPPER PORTION OF LEG MAY BE CUT INTO VEAL STEAKS

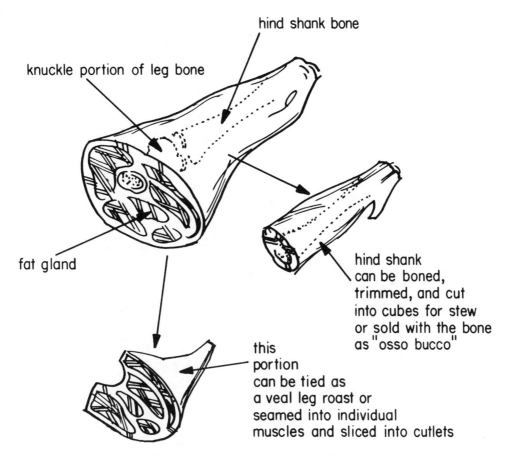

hind shank bone

knuckle portion of leg bone

fat gland

hind shank can be boned, trimmed, and cut into cubes for stew or sold with the bone as "osso bucco"

this portion can be tied as a veal leg roast or seamed into individual muscles and sliced into cutlets

FIG. 11.19. AFTER STEAKS ARE CUT FROM UPPER PORTION OF LEG, REMAINDER CAN BE MERCHANDISED AS SHOWN

3. Remove the bone dust and place the steaks in suitable boats for display and merchandising.

   Note: It is advisable not to cut veal steaks past the fat gland or into the knuckle portion of the leg bone. The remainder of the legs should be boned, trimmed, and merchandised as a roast or sliced into cutlets. This is a matter of store merchandising practice (see Fig. 11.19).

Boning the Leg

1. Place the leg on the bench with the knob of the aitch bone facing up.
2. Remove the flank and flank fat thereby exposing the flesh on the top sirloin portion of the leg (see Fig. 11.20).

   Caution: Do not cut too deep or you will score the lean muscle. This may cause difficulty in slicing the veal cutlets.

   Note: Some meat cutters will remove the entire flank and the flank fat when separating the loin from the hindsaddle. This is a matter of store practice.

3. Loosen and lay back the tenderloin muscle along the side of the pelvic bone. Start with the tip of the boning knife at the knob end of the aitch bone and cut toward the backbone (see Fig. 11.21).

   Caution: Use only the tip of the boning knife in order to avoid scoring the tenderloin muscle and, possibly, the sirloin muscle.

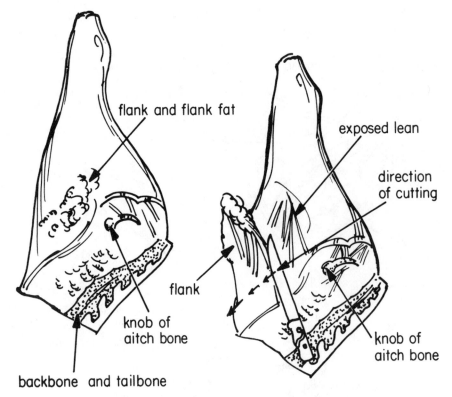

flank and flank fat

exposed lean

direction of cutting

flank

knob of aitch bone

knob of aitch bone

backbone and tailbone

FIG. 11.20. CUT OFF FLANK AND FLANK FAT

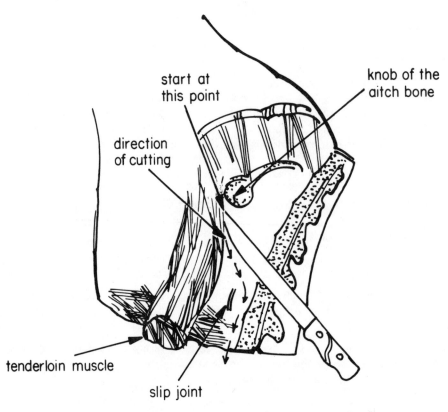

start at this point

knob of the aitch bone

direction of cutting

tenderloin muscle

slip joint

FIG. 11.21. LOOSEN AND LAY BACK TENDERLOIN MUSCLE

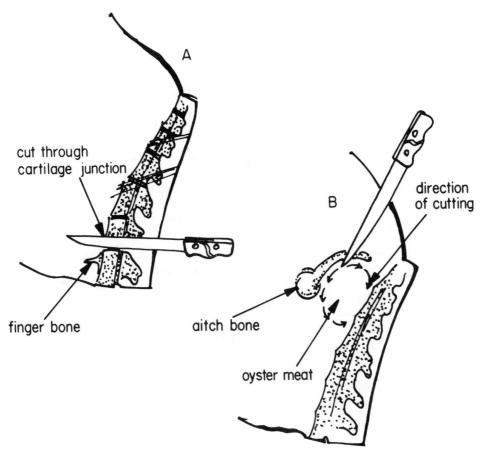

cut through
cartilage junction

finger bone

B

direction
of cutting

aitch bone

oyster meat

FIG. 11.22. REMOVE (A) FINGER BONE AND (B) OYSTER MEAT

Note: This step will expose the slip joint and the last finger bone. These will be
removed later as the veal leg is processed.

4. Cut through the cartilage junction of the backbone (tail) located at the end of
the hip bone. Follow the contour of the finger bone for easy removal of the
bone (see Fig. 11.22A).

Note: Some meat cutters will omit this step and proceed to cut into the slip
joint. This practice is wasteful because of the meat that remains on the
last finger bone. However, this practice exists because of habit and haste
upon the part of the meat cutter.

5. Remove the oyster meat in the cavity of the aitch bone (see Fig. 11.22B).

Note: These trimmings can be used for ground meat items or mixed with other
lean trimmings for patties or cubed steaks.

6. Cut through the slip joint keeping the cutting edge of the knife in the direction
of the backbone. Do not force the knife through the joint. It should slide
through very easily. If it does not, you are probably not cutting in the right
direction which is toward the slip joint. Remove the backbone and tail bone in
one piece (see Fig. 11.23).

Caution: Keep your free hand in back of the cutting edge of the knife while
you are holding the leg in order to cut through the slip joint.

Note: Some meat cutters will remove the backbone and the tail bone attached
to the pelvic bone all in one piece. Again, this is a matter of store procedure and practice.

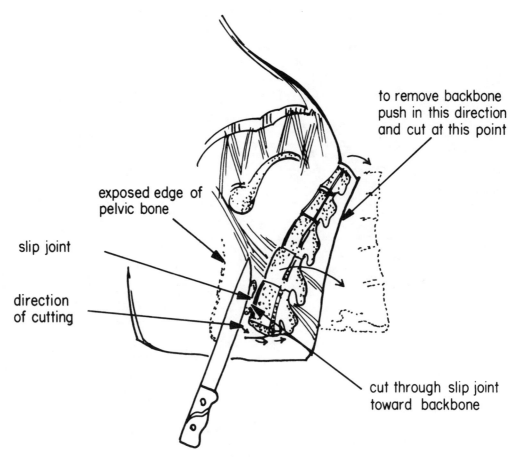

to remove backbone
push in this direction
and cut at this point

exposed edge of
pelvic bone

slip joint

direction
of cutting

cut through slip joint
toward backbone

FIG. 11.23. CUT BACKBONE AND TAIL BONE FREE FROM THE PELVIC BONE

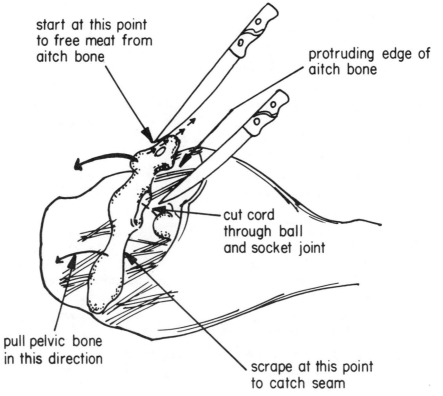

start at this point
to free meat from
aitch bone

protruding edge of
aitch bone

cut cord
through ball
and socket joint

pull pelvic bone
in this direction

scrape at this point
to catch seam

FIG. 11.24. CUT PELVIC BONE FREE FROM LEG

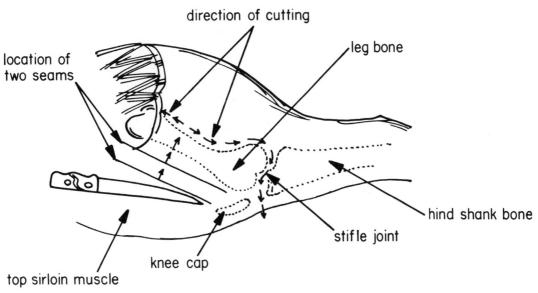

FIG. 11.25. CUT THROUGH SEAM TO UNDERSIDE OF LEG BONE

7. Remove the pelvic bone by cutting close to the knob of the aitch bone and keeping the tip of the boning knife against the bone. Cut the cord through the ball and socket joint. Follow the contour of the bone and use the tip of the knife to free the meat from the protruding edge of the pelvic bone (see Fig. 11.24).

   Caution: Keep your fingers away from the cutting action of the knife.

   Note: The pelvic bone will pull freely from the sirloin portion of the leg if the seam is caught just below the socket portion of the pelvic bone.

8. Locate the two seams on the top sirloin portion of the leg. Cut through one of the natural seams in the direction of the leg bone. Follow the seam to the underside of the leg bone (see Fig. 11.25).

   Note: Avoid cutting through the muscles. These muscles are usually sliced into cutlets.

9. To remove the leg bone, follow the contour of the bone with the tip of the boning knife, cutting from the ball portion of the leg bone to the knuckle

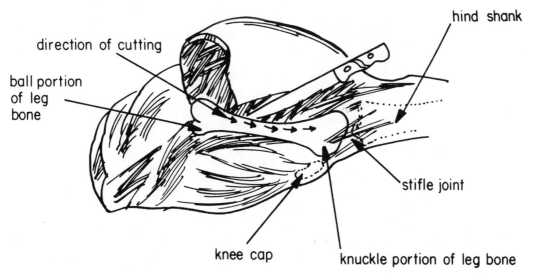

FIG. 11.26. FREE LEG BONE FROM MEAT FOLLOWING DIRECTION OF CUTTING

portion of the leg bone. Separate the leg bone from the hind shank bone by cutting through the stifle joint (see Fig. 11.26).

Note: Some meat cutters will remove the leg and the hind shank bone in one piece. This is determined by the store's merchandising practices. Some stores prefer to cut boneless shins into stew items.

10. In order to free the meat from the hind shank bone, cut on both sides of the hind shank bone to free the shin meat from the entire bone. This procedure is similar to that followed when boning a beef shin.

Seaming the Muscles of the Boneless Leg

1. Remove the tenderloin and flank muscles by starting at the tip of the tenderloin muscle located at the underside of the top sirloin muscle (see Fig. 11.27).

Note: Separate the tenderloin and flank muscle. Trim off the excess fat on the tenderloin muscle and remove the membrane on both sides of the flank muscle.

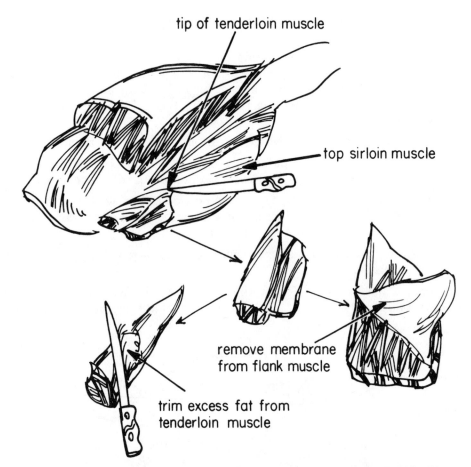

FIG. 11.27. REMOVE TENDERLOIN AND FLANK MUSCLE FROM BONELESS LEG

2. Remove the top round muscle by starting at the center of the leg at the point where the leg bone was removed. Cut into the natural seam between the top round and bottom round (see Fig. 11.28).

Note: Remove the excess fat on the top portion of the top round. Some meat cutters will separate the top round into the two muscles located at the seam which runs lengthwise. This is also a matter of store practice.

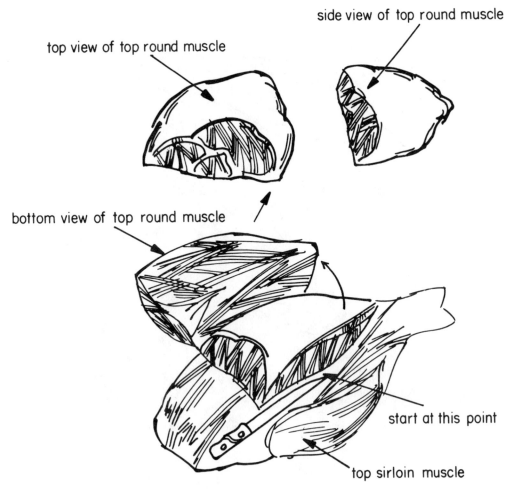

top view of top round muscle

side view of top round muscle

bottom view of top round muscle

start at this point

top sirloin muscle

FIG. 11.28. REMOVE TOP ROUND MUSCLE FROM BONELESS LEG

3. Remove the top sirloin muscle by pulling it free from the leg. Start at the center of the leg where the leg bone was removed. If the cap covering remains on the leg, remove the cap at the natural seam between the cap and the sirloin muscle (see Fig. 11.29).

   Note: Some meat cutters will remove the cap together with the top sirloin. This is also a matter of store practice. Trim the cap covering by removing the fat and membranes. Then remove the knee cap in the top sirloin muscle.

4. Remove the sirloin muscle by starting at the tip of the muscle located at the top of the bottom round which is separated by a fat seam. Trim off the excess fat (see Fig. 11.30).

   Note: The sirloin muscle has a thin layer of lean which is separated by a seam. Some meat cutters may or may not remove this thin layer before slicing.

5. The outside round muscle contains three distinct muscles. These are the eye round, bottom round, and the heel of the round. Remove the heel of the round by starting at the intramuscular fat between the heel and the bottom round. Remove the tendonous muscle and merchandise this cut for veal stew. Separate the heel into two distinct muscles. Separate the eye round from the bottom round at the seam (see Fig. 11.31). Some meat cutters may remove the outside membrane on the side of the bottom round muscle and any excess fat remaining on the muscle.

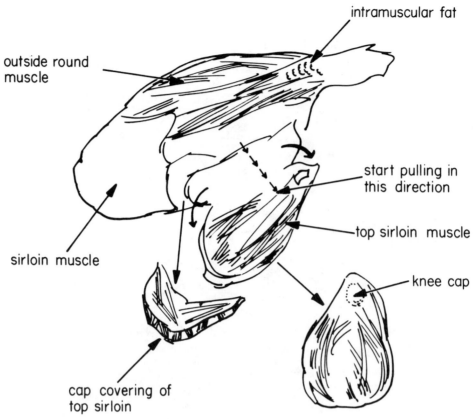

FIG. 11.29. PULL TOP SIRLOIN MUSCLE FREE FROM LEG

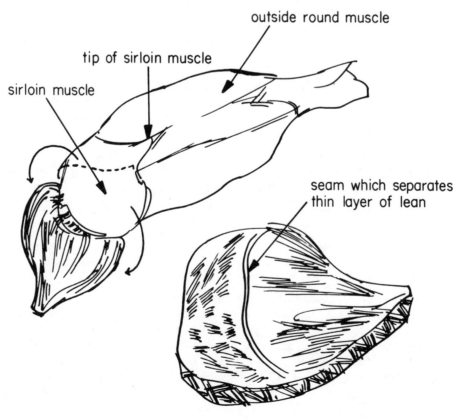

FIG. 11.30. REMOVE SIRLOIN MUSCLE FROM BONELESS LEG

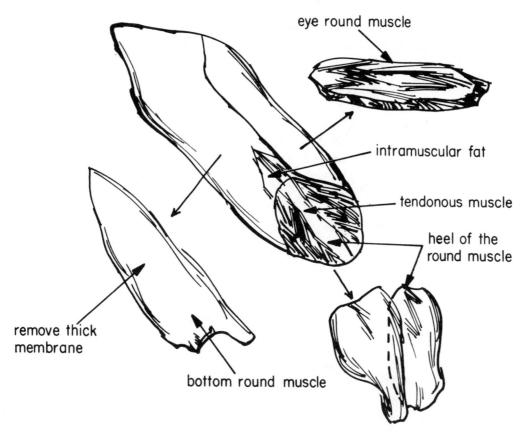

eye round muscle

intramuscular fat

tendonous muscle

heel of the round muscle

remove thick membrane

bottom round muscle

FIG. 11.31. SEPARATE OUTSIDE ROUND INTO THREE MUSCLES: EYE ROUND MUSCLE, BOTTOM ROUND MUSCLE, AND HEEL OF THE ROUND MUSCLE

MERCHANDISING THE BONELESS LEG

Retailers have various methods of merchandising the boneless veal leg. These methods often depend upon consumer demand, supply, and price. The most popular retail meat cut derived from the boneless veal leg is cutlets. One of the highest retail priced meat items in retail stores is that of veal cutlets, cut from the veal leg. Retailers rarely prepare veal roasts from the boneless leg unless it is requested by the customer. Many chains and supermarkets purchase processed veal items from packers and wholesalers. These are veal roasts, veal cutlets, T.B.S.'s (tops, bottoms, and sirloins), veal fillets, veal stew, breaded veal cutlets, veal chops, and others. This is usually due to the high cost of labor, the lack of skill and knowledge of the meat cutter, or a combination of both. The following are some suggested methods for merchandising the boneless veal leg.

SLICING THE BONELESS LEG INTO CUTLETS

Tenderloin and Flank Muscle

1. Separate the tenderloin and flank muscle into two separate pieces. Remove the excess fat and membrane from both pieces. (Refer back to Fig. 11.27.)
2. Slice the tenderloin muscle lengthwise and at a slight angle with the cutting edge of the knife in the direction of the bench (see Fig. 11.32).

    Note: Some retailers may butterfly the tenderloin slices. This is generally determined by the size of the tenderloin muscle. If the muscle is large, meat cutters may slice the tenderloin muscle crosswise instead of lengthwise. The methods used by retailers will vary widely from store to store.

3. Split the flank muscle lengthwise into two or three slices depending upon the thickness of the veal slice (see Fig. 11.32).

    Caution: Care should be taken in the direction of the cutting edge of the knife. Keep the cutting edge of the knife angled toward the bench.

FIG. 11.32. CUTLETS MAY BE MADE FROM TENDERLOIN AND FLANK MUSCLE

Note: Avoid packaging these slices into one boat. It is advisable to mix these slices with various muscles sliced from the boneless leg into one boat. Due to the high cost of veal it is advisable to keep the total weight of the package at 1 lb or under. Many consumers often purchase meat according to the total price of the package, rather than the total weight of the package.

Top Round Muscle

1. Start to cut slices at an angle and at the point of the cut surface where the aitch bone was removed. Remove any discolored meat and membrane before slicing (see Fig. 11.33).

   Note: Slicing at an angle will produce a wider slice of veal.

2. Continue to slice the cutlets to a point approximately ½ or ¾ of the length of the top round muscle (see Fig. 11.33).

   Note: Cut slices approximately ⅛-in. thick.

3. Remove the thin muscle from the top round by cutting through at the natural fat seam. Split the thin muscle into 2 or 3 slices. The remainder of the top round muscle can then be butterflied or sliced lengthwise. This is a matter of store merchandising practice (see Fig. 11.33).

   Note: Some meat cutters will remove the thin muscle before slicing any cutlets from the top round muscle.

Top Sirloin Muscle

The top sirloin muscle can be sliced somewhat similar to that of the top round muscle. It can also be separated into three muscles before slicing. The following is a suggested method.

1. Remove the bottom muscle from the top sirloin at the fat seam located at the bottom of the top sirloin (see Fig. 11.34).

2. Divide the bottom muscle into two separate muscles, starting at the tendonous end (see Fig. 11.34).

   Note: Remove all membranes before slicing into thin veal cutlets.

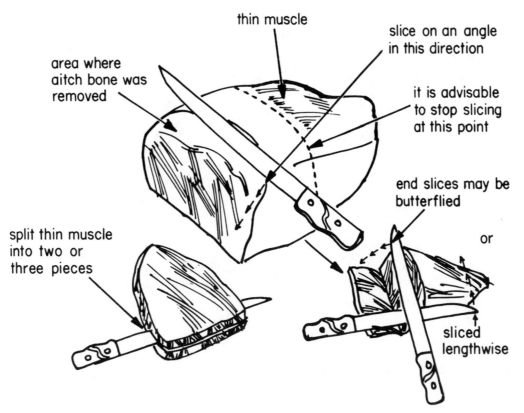

area where
aitch bone was
removed

thin muscle

slice on an angle
in this direction

it is advisable
to stop slicing
at this point

end slices may be
butterflied

or

split thin muscle
into two or
three pieces

sliced
lengthwise

FIG. 11.33. HOW TO CUT VEAL CUTLETS FROM THE TOP ROUND MUSCLE

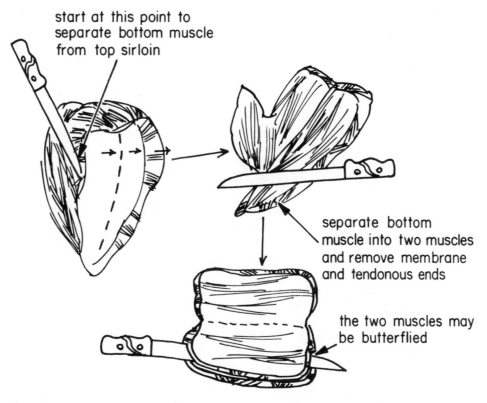

start at this point to
separate bottom muscle
from top sirloin

separate bottom
muscle into two muscles
and remove membrane
and tendonous ends

the two muscles may
be butterflied

FIG. 11.34. HOW TO SLICE CUTLETS FROM THE BOTTOM MUSCLE OF THE TOP SIRLOIN

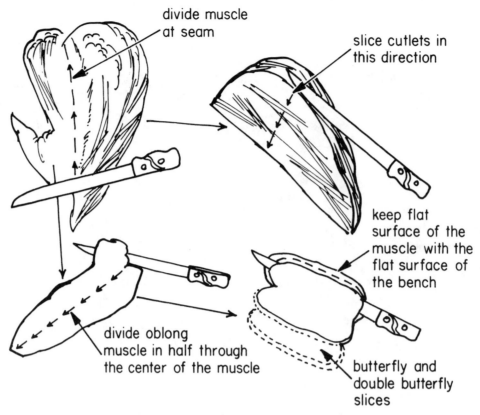

FIG. 11.35. HOW TO MAKE CUTLETS FROM MUSCLES OF THE TOP SIRLOIN

3. Separate the remainder of the top sirloin muscle into two muscles, one oblong and the other shaped like a half moon (see Fig. 11.35).

   Note: Some meat cutters will omit this step and slice the cutlets without separating the muscle. This is a matter of store practice.

4. Split the oblong muscle in half. Slice the cutlets from each half keeping the flat surface of the muscle facing the flat surface of the cutting table (see Fig. 11.35).

   Note: Some meat cutters may double butterfly or triple butterfly each slice, depending upon the size of the muscle.

5. Slice the half-moon shaped muscle from the thick side down to the thin side of the muscle (see Fig. 11.35).

Eye Round Muscle

1. Cut the eye round muscle in half crosswise (see Fig. 11.36).
2. Cut slices lengthwise for single, double, or triple butterflied slices. Keep the knife level with the surface of the table (see Fig. 11.36).

   Note: Some meat cutters will slice from the top of the muscle while others may start at the bottom of the muscle. This is a matter of preference. The ease of handling the muscle by the meat cutter determines the method to be used.

   Caution: Avoid cutting slices with holes in the cutlet. This is due to misjudgement in cutting when butterflying the veal slices.

Bottom Round Muscle

1. Remove the tip on the side of the bottom round muscle located at the natural seam (see Fig. 11.37).

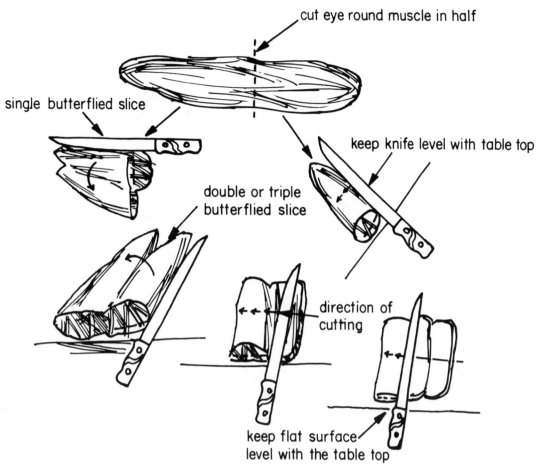

cut eye round muscle in half

single butterflied slice

keep knife level with table top

double or triple
butterflied slice

direction of
cutting

keep flat surface
level with the table top

FIG. 11.36. HOW TO PREPARE CUTLETS FROM THE EYE ROUND MUSCLE

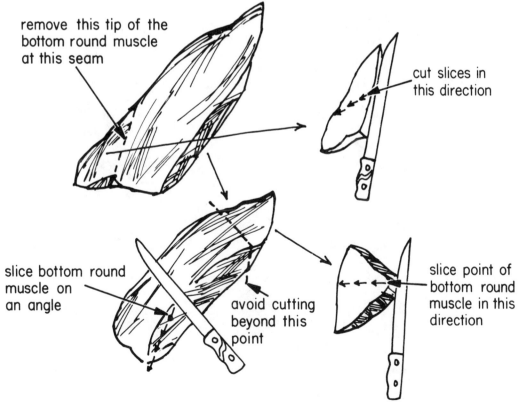

remove this tip of the
bottom round muscle
at this seam

cut slices in
this direction

slice bottom round
muscle on
an angle

avoid cutting
beyond this
point

slice point of
bottom round
muscle in this
direction

FIG. 11.37. HOW TO PREPARE CUTLETS FROM THE BOTTOM ROUND MUSCLE

Note: Some meat cutters will omit this step and begin to slice the cutlets from either end of the bottom round. Not slicing from the heel end with the tip removed, may result in difficulty because of the seam in the bottom round. This membrane may cause irregular slices.

2. Split the tip muscle into 2 or 3 slices, depending upon the thickness and size of the muscle. Cut from the thick side to the thin side for ease of slicing. If the muscle is small, the slices can then be butterflied (see Fig. 11.37).

3. Cut slices from the heel end of the bottom round muscle at an angle to produce wider slices of cutlets (see Fig. 11.37).

    Note: It is advisable not to cut past the point where the bottom round muscle comes to a point (see Fig. 11.37).

    Note: Some meat cutters may or may not slice at an angle and, therefore, butterfly these slices to produce a wider slice. This is a matter of store merchandising practice.

4. Slice the point of the bottom round muscle, starting at the thick end and cutting across the width of the entire muscle (see Fig. 11.37).

Heel of the Round Muscle

1. Separate the heel of the round muscle into two individual muscles at the natural seam (see Fig. 11.38).
2. Remove the membrane from each piece.
3. Slice the oval-shaped muscle across the width of the muscle, keeping the knife level with the surface of the table (see Fig. 11.38).
4. Slice the triangular-shaped muscle from the thick end to the thin end. The last slice can then be butterflied (see Fig. 11.38).

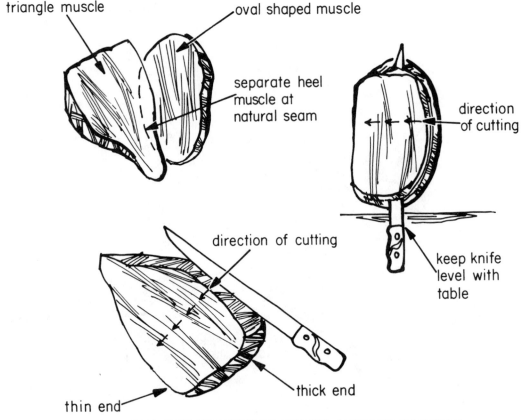

FIG. 11.38. HOW TO SLICE CUTLETS FROM THE HEEL OF THE ROUND MUSCLE

Sirloin Muscle

1. Remove the thin layer of lean on the top surface of the sirloin muscle at the natural seam (see Fig. 11.39).

   Note: Some meat cutters omit this step and begin to slice cutlets. It is advisable to remove this thin layer because of the tough tendons which are in the lean. This muscle contains many tendons because it was connected to the pelvic bone.

2. Slice the cutlets from the thick, round end, not the pointed end. Slice at a slight angle to acquire a wider slice of veal (see Fig. 11.39).

   Note: It is advisable not to cut past the place where the membrane in the point becomes thick.

3. Separate the point of the sirloin muscle into two pieces and remove the membrane. Butterfly both pieces into cutlets. (see Fig. 11.39).

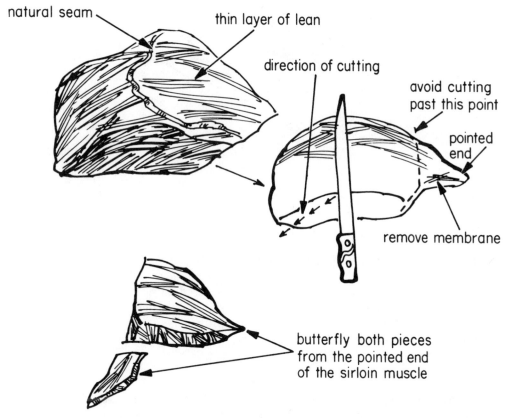

natural seam

thin layer of lean

direction of cutting

avoid cutting past this point

pointed end

remove membrane

butterfly both pieces from the pointed end of the sirloin muscle

FIG. 11.39. HOW TO SLICE CUTLETS FROM THE SIRLOIN MUSCLE

TIEING THE BONELESS LEG INTO A ROAST

Retailers rarely process roasts from the veal legs because the selling price of veal cutlets is higher and therefore offers the retailer a higher percentage of profit. There are many factors which a retailer will take into consideration before merchandising roasts from the veal leg. Some of the principal factors are:

1. The wholesale price of veal.
2. The class and quality of veal.
3. The size and weight of the veal legs.
4. The ratio of the lean to bone.

Some retailers may purchase legs of lower grades, or veal of lighter weights, such as bob veal. Other retailers may use only heavier types of veal for roasts. This is

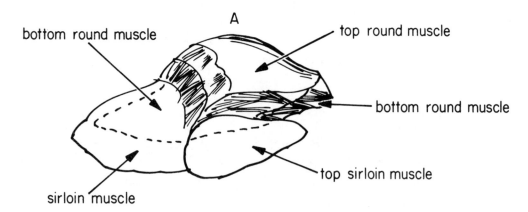

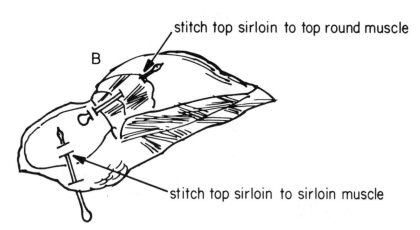

FIG. 11.40. REMOVE TOP SIRLOIN MUSCLE (A) AND STITCH IT (B) TO THE SIRLOIN AND TOP
ROUND MUSCLES

generally a matter of store buying and merchandising practice. There are variations
from store to store.

Hotels, restaurants, and institutions are considered to be the principal buyers of
boneless veal leg roasts processed by packers and wholesalers. However, it is necessary for meat cutters to acquire the skills and knowledge in processing veal leg roasts
by employing various methods. The following are some suggested methods.

Method No. 1

1. Remove the top sirloin muscle by seaming the muscle from the bottom round
   muscle portion of the leg. See Fig. 11.40A.

   Note: Check to see that the knee cap bone has been removed during the boning
   process. If not remove the bone before tieing the roast.

2. Place the top sirloin muscle on the top portion of the sirloin muscle (see Fig.
   11.40B).
3. Stitch the top sirloin muscle to the sirloin and top round muscle as shown in
   Fig. 11.40B.
4. Reverse the leg so that the smooth outer surface (skin side) is facing up.
5. Place two loose guide strings on the leg lengthwise (Fig. 11.41A).
6. Place evenly-spaced cross strings about 1 to 1½ in. apart (see Fig. 11.41B).

   Note: Keep the knots on the bottom of the roast. Large veal legs can be cut
   into 2 or 3 pieces depending upon the weight of the roast desired by
   store merchandising practice.

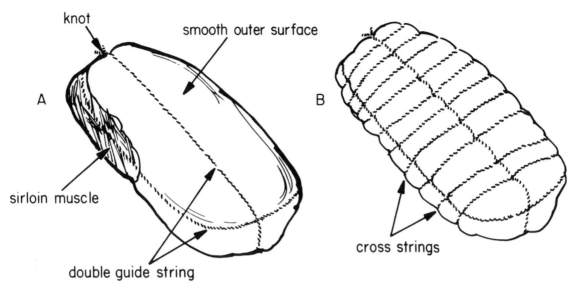

FIG. 11.41. TO SHAPE THE BONELESS VEAL LEG, PLACE GUIDE STRINGS (A) AROUND LENGTH AND CROSS STRINGS (B) AROUND CIRCUMFERENCE

Method No. 2

1. Remove the top sirloin muscle by following step No. 1 in method No. 1.
2. Cut through the bottom round muscle by starting the cut at the top round muscle in order to separate the sirloin and point of the bottom round muscle. (see Fig. 11.42A).

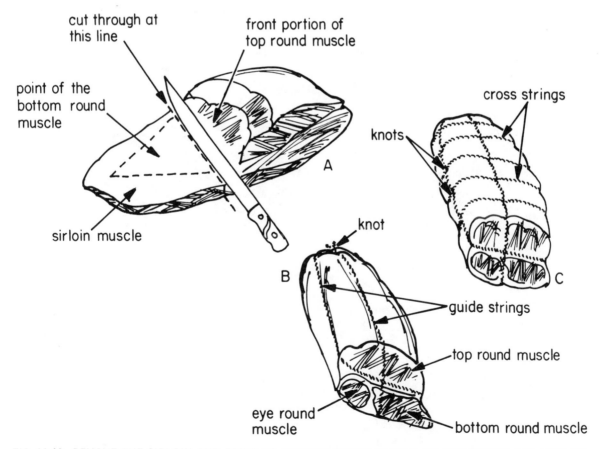

FIG. 11.42. REMOVE THE SIRLOIN AND POINT OF BOTTOM ROUND MUSCLE (A) AND TIE TOP AND BOTTOM ROUND MUSCLE (B) AS A ROAST WITH (C) GUIDE STRINGS AND CROSS STRINGS

Note: Some meat cutters may use the top sirloin and sirloin muscle for cutting thin cutlets rather than tieing another roast from these cut muscles. The merchandising practice of each store will determine whether the muscle cut from the veal leg will be used for cutlets or a roast.

3. Place one or two guide strings lengthwise on the remainder of the veal leg (Fig. 11.42B).
4. Place evenly-spaced cross strings about 1 to 1½ in. apart (see Fig. 11.42C).

Method No. 3

1. Follow step No. 1 and 2 in method No. 2.
2. Stitch the top sirloin muscle to the sirloin muscle as shown in Fig. 11.43A.
3. Place one guide string on the top and bottom portion of the roast (see Fig. 11.43B).

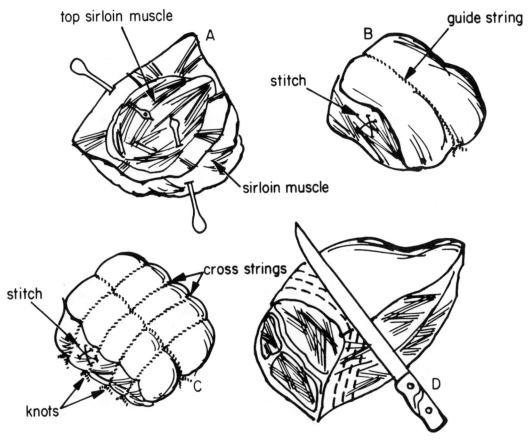

FIG. 11.43. TIE TOP SIRLOIN AND SIRLOIN MUSCLE (A) INTO A ROAST WITH GUIDE STRING (B) AND CROSS STRINGS (C) WITH REMAINDER OF THE VEAL LEG (D) SLICED INTO CUTLETS

4. Place evenly-spaced cross strings 1 to 1½ in. apart. Start at the thickest part of the roast to shape the roast evenly (see Fig. 11.43C).
5. The remainder of the leg (top and bottom round) can be sliced into cutlets as shown in Fig. 11.43D, or tied into a roast by following step No. 4 in method 2.

   Note: If the store is equipped with a tieing machine or a Jet-Net machine, follow the same steps for stitching but omit the guide strings and cross strings.

UNIT 12: Veal Foresaddles

The veal foresaddle will vary from 49 to 52% of the veal carcass depending upon the method used in cutting the carcass perpendicular to the backbone. Packers will generally cut veal foresaddles from the veal carcass by cutting between the 12th and 13th rib bone. Wholesalers vary their methods and may cut between the 10th and 11th rib bone, or cut between the 11th and 12th rib bone. The method employed by the wholesaler is generally determined by the price factor. It is important to remember that veal foresaddles cost approximately 50¢ per lb less than veal hindsaddles. This price differential will often cause variations in wholesale cutting.

Chain stores and supermarkets in various regions of the country generally cut veal foresaddles into retail cuts, which are somewhat similar to that of the lamb foresaddle. This type of merchandising may be feasible for veal foresaddles of lighter weights. However, veal foresaddles of heavier weights should be cut into smaller subprimal cuts, because of its large size, and then processed into smaller retail cuts. This unit will explain various methods of cutting and merchandising veal foresaddles into retail cuts.

The veal foresaddles contain a large percentage of bones. Retailers generally purchase only those wholesale cuts from the veal foresaddle which are popular according to consumer demands. First let us examine the bone structure of the veal foresaddle (see Fig. 12.1).

The bones contained in the veal foresaddle are: the backbone, (chine and feather), the rib bones, the breast bone, the neck bones, the shank, the arm, and the blade bone. Refer back to primal and subprimal cuts of veal, Fig. 10.1 through 10.3 in Unit 10 to refresh your memory with the various cuts.

When veal foresaddles are broken down into primal and subprimal cuts in the New York Metropolitan area, the lifted veal shoulders will yield approximately 30% of the foresaddle. The veal breasts will yield 18%. The veal racks and veal necks will vary from 24 to 26% each, depending upon the removal of short or long veal racks. The retail cuts which are derived from the veal foresaddle will vary widely from store to store, depending upon the region of the country. The following are some suggested methods for processing and merchandising the veal foresaddle.

PROCESSING THE VEAL BREAST

The subprimal cut of veal breast will consist of various forms and weights depending on how they were processed from the veal foresaddles. Packers generally cut a small veal breast because packers remove the veal rack (double) 4 in. from the rib eye muscle. Wholesalers and retailers first remove the lifted veal shoulder and then cut only 2 in. from the rib eye muscle. This will produce a larger veal breast because of the extra length of rib bones attached to the breast (see Fig. 12.2). This type of merchandising is generally performed in the northeastern part of the country. This is due to the popular retail cuts which are derived from the lifted veal shoulder and racks. This will be discussed further in the latter part of this unit.

Veal Breast With Pocket

1. Place the veal breast on the cutting table with the breast bone facing up (see Fig. 12.3).
2. Remove the thin strip along the ventral edge and the edge of the skirt section from the veal breast (see Fig. 12.3).

   Note: This will allow for the easy removal of the thin membrane.

3. Remove the thin membrane from the top portion of the skirt and false skirt section. Start at the breast bone area for easy removal (see Fig. 12.3).
4. Reverse the position of the veal breast on the cutting table so that the breast bone is facing the table and the pointed end is away from you (see Fig. 12.4).
5. With the steak knife, open a pocket on the thin end of the breast. Keep the

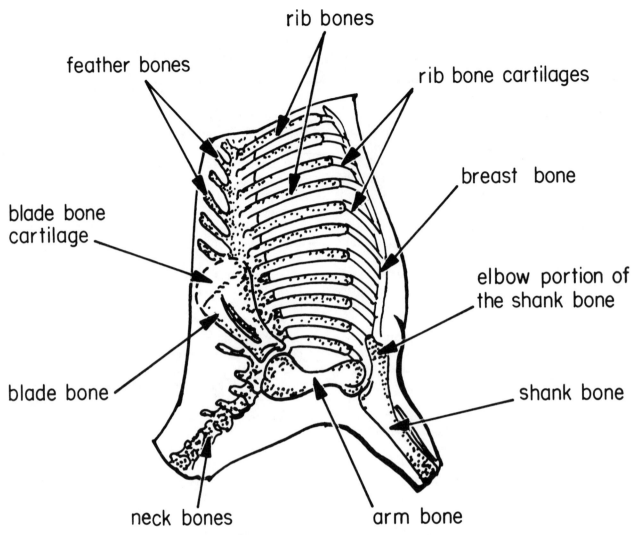

FIG. 12.1. BONE STRUCTURE OF THE VEAL FORESADDLE

cutting edge of the knife close to the rib bones while forming a pocket (see Fig. 12.4).

Note: It is advisable to place a small piece of white paper exposed from the pocket so consumers can easily locate the opening. Avoid cutting too close to the breast bone area. This may cause stuffing to seep out during the cooking process.

6. Crack the breast bone by cutting through the bone on the band saw (see Fig. 12.5).

Caution: Keep your fingers clear from the path of the blade.

Note: Avoid cutting past the breast bone. You may be cutting into the precut pocket. Try to cut through the breast bone in the same line with the finger meat. This will assist the consumer in slicing the cooked breast.

Boning a Veal Breast

1. Follow steps No. 1 through No. 3 above in processing a veal breast with a pocket.

Note: Some meat cutters will omit these steps before boning, and some may follow these steps after the boning procedure. This is a matter of preference by the meat cutter.

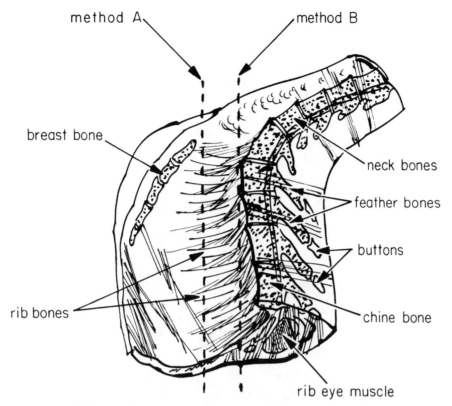

method A   method B

breast bone

neck bones

feather bones

buttons

rib bones

chine bone

rib eye muscle

FIG. 12.2. GENERALLY, PACKERS CUT THE BREAST 4 INCHES FROM THE RIB EYE
MUSCLE (A) WHILE WHOLESALERS AND RETAILERS REMOVE A LARGER BREAST
(B) CUTTING ONLY 2 INCHES FROM RIB EYE MUSCLE

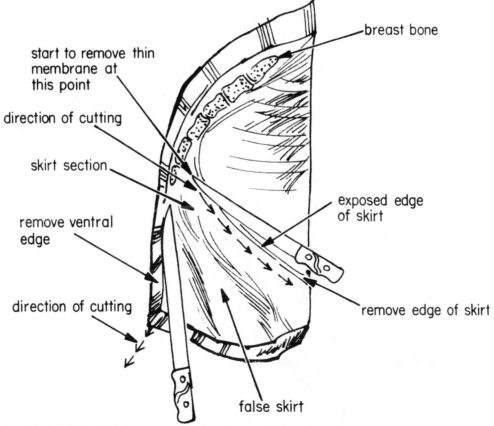

breast bone

start to remove thin
membrane at
this point

direction of cutting

skirt section

exposed edge
of skirt

remove ventral
edge

direction of cutting

remove edge of skirt

false skirt

FIG. 12.3. DIRECTION OF CUTTING TO REMOVE VENTRAL EDGE AND EXPOSED EDGE OF
SKIRT FROM BREAST

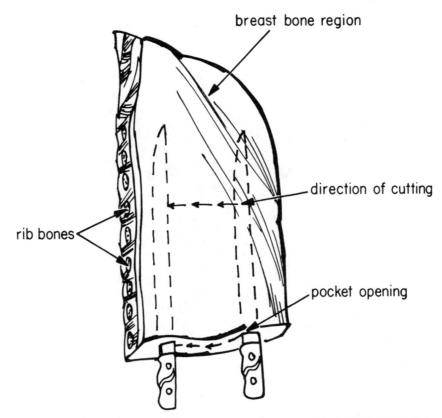

FIG. 12.4. DIRECTION OF CUTTING TO MAKE POCKET IN BREAST FOR STUFFING

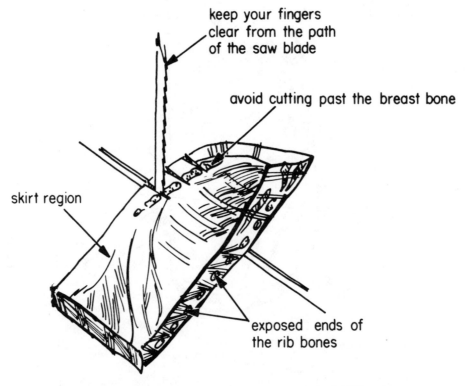

FIG. 12.5. CUT BREAST BONE ON THE BAND SAW

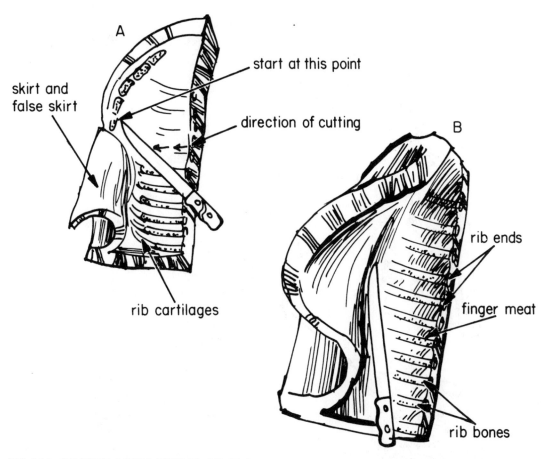

FIG. 12.6. TO BONE A VEAL BREAST: (A) FIRST LAY BACK SKIRT AND FALSE SKIRT, THEN BY CUT-
TING CLOSE TO THE BONES (B) REMOVE RIB BONES AND CARTILAGES IN ONE PIECE

2. Loosen and lay back the skirt and false skirt section of the breast past the rib
   bone cartilages (see Fig. 12.6A).

   Note: Start to cut at the point of the breast bone area.

3. Starting at the rib bone ends, cut close to the rib bones and past the rib bone
   cartilages down to the breast bone. Remove the bones in one piece (see Fig.
   12.6B).

   Caution: Keep your fingers behind the cutting action of the knife.

   Note: Do not discard these bones. Remove the finger meat between the rib
   bones and merchandise these trimmings for any ground veal item.

Merchandising Variations

The boneless veal breast can be rolled single or double. It can be rolled lengthwise
or crosswise. The breast can also be stuffed with a prepared mixture before rolling.
The boneless breast can also be cubed for veal stew; it is advisable to mix cubed
breast with diced shanks and shins of veal. The boneless breast can be sliced and put
through a steak tenderizing machine and merchandised as a cubed veal steak. It can
also be ground with other trimmings and made into patties or a meat loaf item (see
Fig. 12.7).

Meat cutters should change their methods of merchandising the veal breast to
assist their customers in a variety of veal menu dishes. Do not stick to one method
of cutting. Customers like new displays. It entices the consumer to make a visual
inspection of all the displayed items. This encourages impulse buying and may increase your tonnage of rough cuts from the veal foresaddle.

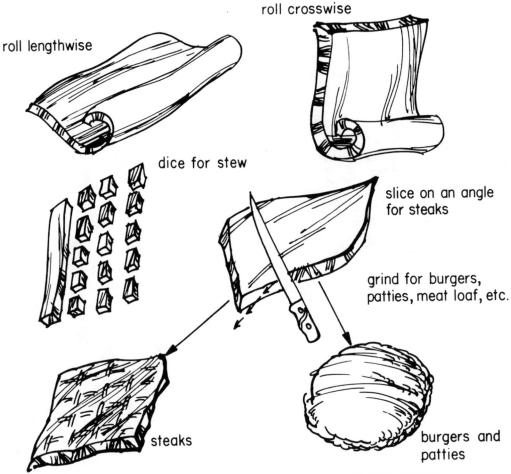

FIG. 12.7. MERCHANDISING VARIATIONS FOR BONELESS VEAL BREAST

PROCESSING THE VARIOUS TYPES OF VEAL RACKS

Basically, there are three different types of veal racks. Packers will generally cut veal racks which contain 14 rib bones (double rack, hotel style). Wholesalers and retailers cut short and long veal racks. Refer back to primal and subprimal cuts of veal and see method A and method B in Fig. 12.2. The hotel style rack (single) is somewhat similar to that of the set of ribs in beef. However, it is much smaller in size; but the muscle structure is the same. The long and short veal racks have part of the middle chuck muscles in the rack and are minus the top chuck muscle. Part of the deckle is missing in the long and short veal rack because of the removal of the lifted veal shoulder. The main retail cuts derived from these racks are called rib veal chops. However, there are various methods in cutting these racks. The following are some suggested methods in cutting and merchandising veal racks.

Processing Hotel-Style Racks into Chops

1. Place the veal rack on the movable table of the band saw with the bone side up (see Fig. 12.8).
2. Cut down the center of the backbone. Hold both sides of the rack to prevent the rack from rolling (see Fig. 12.8).

Caution: Keep your fingers clear from the path of the blade.

Note: Some meat cutters cut the rack from the blade side first, while others may start with the loin side first. This is a matter of cutter's preference.

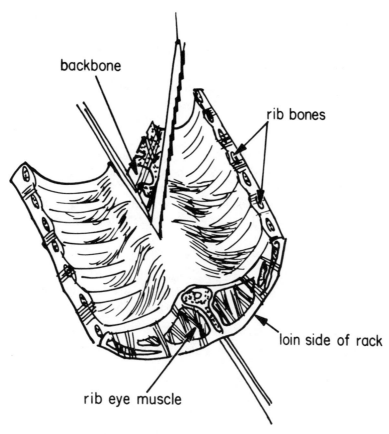

backbone

rib bones

loin side of rack

rib eye muscle

FIG. 12.8. WITH BONE SIDE UP, CUT RACK DOWN CENTER OF BACKBONE

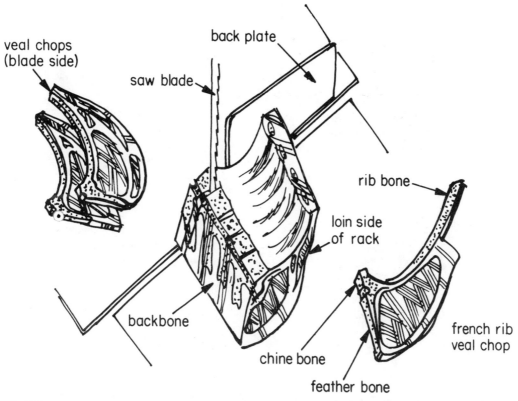

veal chops (blade side)

back plate

saw blade

rib bone

loin side of rack

backbone

chine bone

feather bone

french rib veal chop

FIG. 12.9. WITH BONE SIDE OF RACK ENTERING BLADE OF BAND SAW FIRST, CUT RIB CHOPS OF DESIRED THICKNESS

3. Place the single rack on the movable carriage of the band saw with the backbone facing the blade (see Fig. 12.9).
4. Cut the chops at the desired thickness with the bone side (backbone) entering the blade first. Guide chops through the blade with your left hand.

Caution: Keep your fingers clear from the path of the blade. Keep the rack flat against the back plate to cut evenly-shaped chops. Do not use any excess pressure. Let the saw do the work. Do not force chops through the blade.

Note: Remove the bone dust from the chops and place them into various size boats. Try to mix chops from both sides of the rack—the blade and loin side—for even distribution. The first 3 or 4 chops cut from the loin side can also be made into a French veal chop. This is accomplished by removing 1 to 2 in. of the flesh from the rib end bone (see Fig. 12.9).

Processing Hotel-Style Racks into Boneless Roasts

1. Place the rack on the bench with the blade side toward you (see Fig. 12.10A).
2. Insert the tip of the boning knife under the blade bone cartilage and follow the contour of the blade bone cartilage (see Fig. 12.10A).

Note: Avoid leaving any portion of the blade bone cartilage in the veal rack.

3. Remove the rib and feather bones starting at the point where the cut rib bone

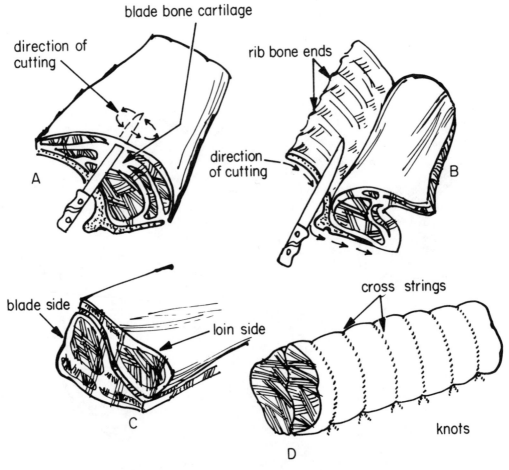

FIG. 12.10. TO PREPARE A BONELESS RACK ROAST, FIRST REMOVE BLADE BONE CARTILAGE (A), THEN SCALP THE RACK (B), PUT TWO RACKS TOGETHER WITH OPPOSITE ENDS FACING EACH OTHER (C) AND TIE (D) WITH CROSS STRINGS

ends are exposed. Cut close to the flat surface of the rib bones and down to the backbone (see Fig. 12.10B).

Note: This method of boning is known as scalping. Remove the back strap.

4. Reverse the position of two boneless veal racks so that opposite ends are facing each other. (See Fig. 12.10C.)

Note: Some meat cutters may prefer to use only one boneless veal rack instead of two depending upon the size and weight of the desired roast.

5. Tie evenly-spaced cross strings, girthwise (see Fig. 12.10D).

Note: If large racks are used it is advisable to cut roast in half for consumers with small families to choose from.

Processing Hotel-Style Racks into Bone-In Roasts

1. Follow steps No. 1 through No. 3 under "Processing Hotel Style Rack into Chops."
2. Saw through the backbone of the rack. Cut between each rib bone. (Refer back to Fig. 12.9.)

Caution: Care should be taken in removing the veal rack from each cut portion of the backbone. The backbone may catch or snag on the back portion of the blade causing the blade to slip off the wheel. This loud noise may alarm the meat cutter causing an accident.

Note: Some retailers may remove the protruding edge of the chine bone before cracking the backbone. This is a matter of store merchandising practice.

Processing Hotel-Style Rack into a Veal Fillet

A veal fillet is actually the rib eye muscle of the veal rack processed from either a 7-rib rack, an 8-rib rack, or the 11-rib rack.

The word fillet as defined in the dictionary means a small piece or strip of boneless meat or fish. The word "fillet" derives from the French and should be used in cooking terms, not meat items, to avoid consumer confusion. The meat industry should identify retail cuts by first naming the meat muscle structure and then by its cooking term or use. An example would be "Chuck Strips for Pepper Steak," or "Flank Steak for Pepper Steak." Retailers often label the package only with the words "Pepper Steak." This type of merchandising would offer the consumer a choice of items to choose from according to their needs.

Veal fillets are generally processed from the long or short rack. They are boneless veal racks with the flank edge and back strap removed. Retailers are reluctant to process boneless racks from the hotel style veal rack (single). This may be due to the high cost of labor or lack of skill and knowledge of the meat cutter. However, it is important to remember that knowledge in all phases of cutting is important in meat merchandising. A meat cutter should know how to prepare or cut various retail items from one wholesale cut.

Follow steps No. 1 through No. 3 given above in "Processing Hotel Style Racks into Boneless Roasts."

1. Remove the flank edge by cutting lengthwise leaving the lip meat on the loin side and removing the lip meat on the blade side (see Fig. 12.11A and 12.11B).

Note: Some meat cutters will cut the flank edge from the boneless rack by measuring 1 in. from the rib eye muscle. This is a matter of store practice.

The merchandising of the veal fillet will vary from store to store. The boneless fillet can be sliced into boneless rib veal chops (see Fig. 12.11C). The veal fillet can also be sliced into thin cutlets (see Fig. 12.11D). Some meat cutters may tie the boneless veal fillets (single or double) into roasts. However, it is important to remember that the selling price of sliced veal fillets is higher than boneless veal roast.

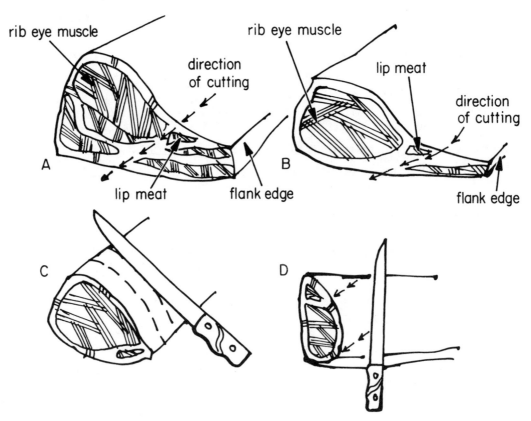

FIG. 12.11. TO MERCHANDISE THE VEAL FILLET: A AND B SHOW WHERE TO CUT AND DIRECTION OF CUTTING TO TRIM THE BONELESS FILLET; THEN CUT CHOPS (C) OR SLICE (D) THIN CUTLETS

The methods of trim and slicing fillets vary widely. Again, this is a matter of store practice.

PROCESSING THE 8-RIB AND THE 11-RIB VEAL RACK

Merchandising the 8- or 11-rib veal rack is similar to the 7-rib veal rack (Hotel-Style). The main difference between the Hotel-Style rack and the 8- or the 11-rib rack is the omission of the top chuck muscles and the addition of the bottom chuck muscle on the 8- and the 11-rib rack. (See Fig. 12.12.) Retailers who purchase extra veal racks from wholesalers in the New York metropolitan area generally purchase the 8-rib veal rack. This is generally due to the method the wholesaler may use in breaking down veal foresaddles.

1. To process rib chops from the 8- or the 11-rib veal rack follow steps No. 1 through No. 4 in "Processing Hotel-Style Racks into Chops."

    Note: Some meat cutters may process a special French veal chop from the last three ribs on the rack. This will be discussed in the latter part of this unit for processing a veal neck.

2. To process the 8- or the 11-rib rack into a boneless veal roast follow steps No. 1 through No. 5 in "Processing Hotel-Style Racks into Boneless Roasts."
3. To process the 8- or the 11-rib rack into a bone-in veal rack roast follow steps No. 1 and 2 in "Processing Hotel-Style Racks into Bone-In Roasts."
4. To process the rack into a veal fillet (rib eye muscle) follow the same procedure in "Processing Hotel-Style Rack into a Veal Fillet."

PROCESSING THE LIFTED VEAL SHOULDER

Lifted shoulders are removed from the veal fore-saddle. They represent approximately 30% of the foresaddle. Packers vary their methods of cutting and merchandising the shoulder. The variation in

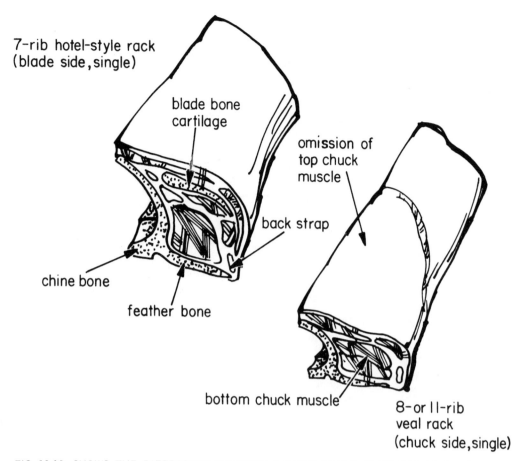

7-rib hotel-style rack
(blade side, single)

blade bone
cartilage

omission of
top chuck
muscle

back strap

chine bone

feather bone

bottom chuck muscle

8- or 11-rib
veal rack
(chuck side, single)

FIG. 12.12. SHOWS THE DIFFERENCE BETWEEN A HOTEL-STYLE RACK AND AN 8- OR 11-RIB
VEAL RACK

processing usually depends upon the region of the country in which the packer is located and is in accordance with the vendors' merchandising needs. Some packers may cut lifted veal shoulders to process veal clods. Others may process veal clods from the square-cut chuck. Chain stores and supermarkets are presently purchasing fully processed and packaged veal retail items processed by packers or wholesalers. These are packed in various weights and placed in cardboard boxes. Some supervisors and managers claim that this type of merchandising and buying will eliminate some of the high costs of labor. This may not be true in each instance. Some meat cutters may not be knowledgable and skilled in the processing and merchandising of retail items from the lifted veal shoulder. This unit will explain the variations in cutting and merchandising the lifted veal shoulder.

Examine the bone structure of the lifted veal shoulder (see Fig. 12.13). The bones contained in the lifted shoulder are the shank bone, the arm bone, and the blade bone with a portion of the cartilage attached to the blade bone. The amount of cartilage and surrounding meat left on the shoulder will depend upon the method of cutting. The lifted shoulder is somewhat similar to that of the long beef shoulder except for the fact that it is smaller in size and weight because of the immaturity of the animal. The average weight of the lifted shoulder varies from 8 to 10 lb. Some shoulders may be larger in size and weight. This will depend upon the maturity of the animal. Following are suggested methods of merchandising the lifted veal shoulder.

PROCESSING SHOULDER STEAKS FROM THE LIFTED VEAL SHOULDER

1. Place the shoulder on the movable carriage of the band saw with the blade bone facing the back plate. (See Fig. 12.14A.)
2. Cut steaks at the desired thickness (approximately ¾ in.) up to the arm bone socket (Fig. 12.14A).

Caution: Keep your fingers clear from the path of the blade.

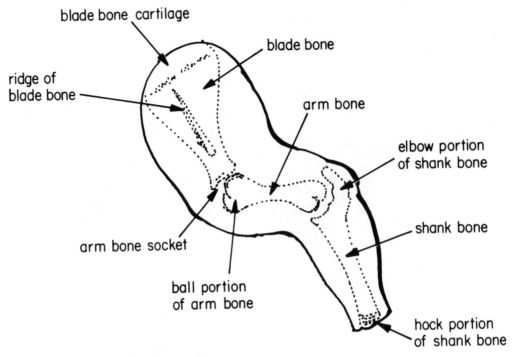

blade bone cartilage

blade bone

ridge of
blade bone

arm bone

elbow portion
of shank bone

shank bone

arm bone socket

ball portion
of arm bone

hock portion
of shank bone

FIG. 12.13. BONE STRUCTURE OF THE LIFTED VEAL SHOULDER

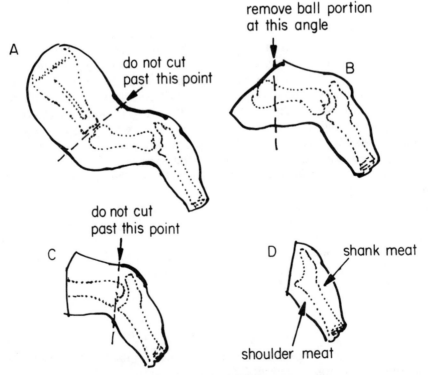

A

do not cut
past this point

remove ball portion
at this angle

B

do not cut
past this point

C

D

shank meat

shoulder meat

FIG. 12.14. TO CUT VEAL SHOULDER STEAKS: (A) CUT BLADE SECTION UP TO
THE ARM BONE SOCKET, THEN (B) REMOVE BALL PORTION AT CORRECT
ANGLE AND (C) CONTINUE TO CUT STEAKS UP TO THE ELBOW PORTION OF
THE SHANK BONE; REMAINDER OF THE SHOULDER (D) MAY BE BONED OR
MERCHANDISED WITH THE BONE IN

Note: The cut veal steaks are somewhat similar to the top chuck steaks cut from the top chuck section of the beef arm chuck. The muscle structure is the same except that they are much smaller in size. Some meat cutters may continue to slice veal shoulder steaks to the elbow portion of the shank bone at the same angle as shown in Fig. 12.14A. This is not advisable because of the large amount of bone in the ball portion of the arm bone.

3. Remove the ball portion of the shoulder as shown in Fig. 12.14B.

Note: Remove the meat from the ball portion of the bone and the tendons attached to the meat. The boneless veal can then be cut into cubes and merchandised as a veal stew item or veal cube steak.

4. Continue to cut veal shoulder steaks at the desired thickness up to the elbow portion of the shank bone (Fig. 12.14C).

Note: The cut steaks resemble the arm steaks cut from beef shoulders. It is advisable to mix the arm cut steaks with cut steaks from the blade section of the shoulder. This is a matter of store practice.

5. The remainder of the shoulder may be boned and the shank and shoulder meat trimmed and cut into cubes for a veal stew item, or ground for a meat loaf item, depending upon the current need of the consumer (see Fig. 12.14D).

BONING THE LIFTED VEAL SHOULDER

Method No. 1

1. Place the shoulder on the bench with the outside surface facing the bench. Keep the hock portion of the shank bone away from you and the shank bone parallel to your body. (See Fig. 12.15A.)

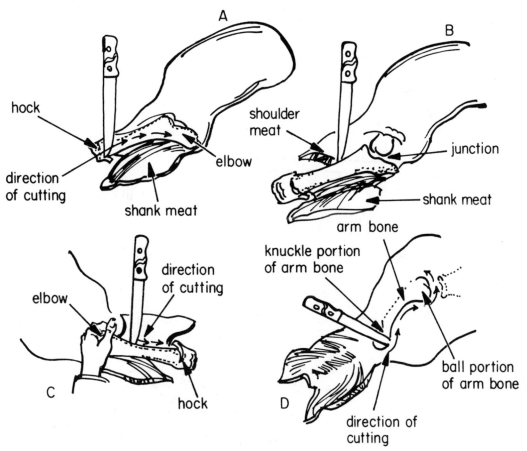

FIG. 12.15. STEPS TO TAKE TO REMOVE SHANK AND ARM BONE

2. Loosen and lay back the shank meat starting at the hock end of the bone and cutting toward the elbow portion of the shank bone (Fig. 12.15A).

   Caution: Keep the tip of the knife against the bone and follow the contour of the bone. Keep your free hand behind the cutting action of the knife. Loosen all the meat around the elbow portion of the shank bone.

3. Loosen the shoulder meat from the opposite side of the shank bone. Start boning at the hock end up to the junction between the shank and arm bone. (See Fig. 12.15B.)

4. Cut through the thin membrane at the junction between the shank and arm bone. Expose the junction by breaking through at this point.

5. Hold the elbow portion of the shank bone in your free hand and free all the meat from the opposite side of the bone by cutting down toward the hock end of the shank bone. (See Fig. 12.15C.)

   Caution: Cut away from your body.

6. Cut along the side of the arm bone to the arm bone socket cutting through the socket. Loosen all the meat from the bone by cutting from the knuckle portion to the ball portion of the arm bone. (See Fig. 12.15D.)

   Note: Some meat cutters may prefer to remove the shank and arm bone in one piece. This is a matter of store practice.

7. Loosen all the meat around the socket portion of the blade bone. Keep the tip of the knife against the flat surface of the blade bone. Loosen the thin muscle on the flat surface of the blade bone down to the cartilage end of the bone (see Fig. 12.16A).

   Caution: Keep your fingers away from the cutting action of the knife.

8. Loosen all the meat from the point of the portion of the ridge on the blade bone. Catch the seam at this point. (See Fig. 12.16B.)

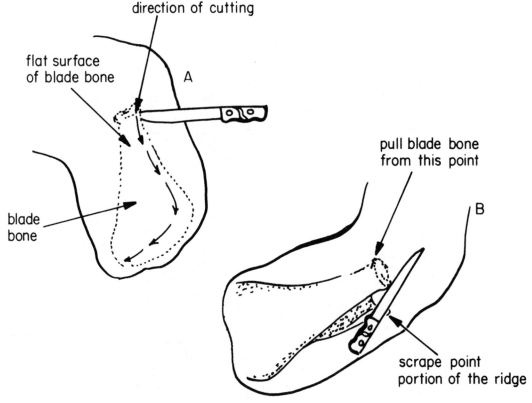

FIG. 12.16. STEPS TO TAKE TO REMOVE BLADE BONE

9. Pull the blade bone free from the shoulder by holding the bone at the socket portion.

   Note: It is advisable to see that the seams are caught on both sides of the blade bone and at the point of the ridge before attempting to pull the bone free from the meat. The bone may snap off leaving the cartilage on the shoulder. Remove cartilage with boning knife.

Method No. 2 (Tunnel)

1. Follow steps No. 1 through No. 5 in method No. 1 in boning the lifted veal shoulder.
2. Tunnel out the arm bone keeping the tip of the boning knife against the bone, and cutting through the arm bone socket (see Fig. 12.17A).

   Caution: Keep your fingers away from the cutting action of the knife.

   Note: It is advisable to invert the shoulder meat as you proceed to remove the bones. Some meat cutters will cut through the clod muscle (cross rib) to make the pocket larger and easier for the removal of the arm bone. Some meat cutters do not tunnel out the arm bone because they only merchandise the blade portion of the veal shoulder as a pocket for stuffing. This is a matter of store merchandising practice.

3. Cut around the socket portion of the blade bone catching the seam around the entire neck portion and point of the ridge on the blade bone. (See Fig. 12.17B.)
4. Pull the blade bone from the shoulder continuing to invert the veal shoulder. Blade cartilage will snap off leaving the cartilage in the shoulder.

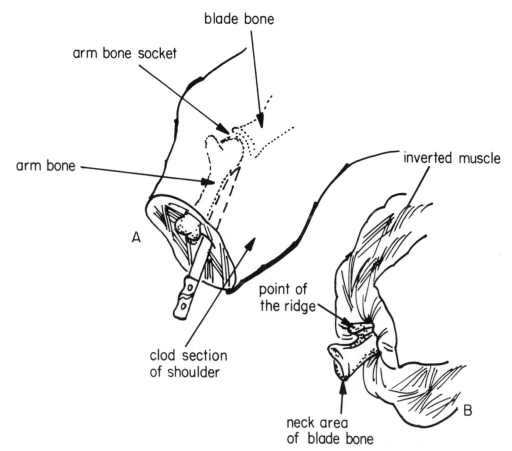

FIG. 12.17. TUNNEL OUT BOTH THE ARM BONE AND THE BLADE BONE

Note: Some meat cutters prefer to hang the shoulder with heavy twine around the neck portion of the blade bone to pull the shoulder free from the blade bone. Some meat cutters may leave the cartilage in the shoulder while others may remove the cartilage. This is a matter of store practice.

5. To merchandise the boneless veal shoulder with the pocket for stuffing, it is advisable to remove the shank and shoulder meat as shown in Fig. 12.18. The shank and shoulder meat can be used for other boneless retail items.

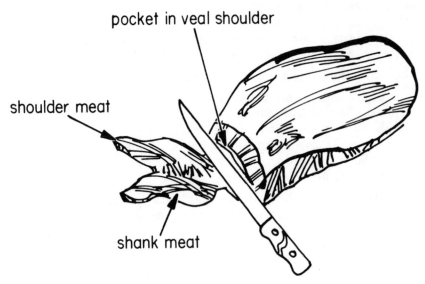

FIG. 12.18.   REMOVE THE SHANK AND THE SHOULDER MEAT

TIEING THE BONELESS LIFTED SHOULDER INTO A ROAST

1. Remove the shank meat as shown in Fig. 12.19A.

   Note: The shank meat should be trimmed of all tendons before merchandising as a veal stew item or other retail items derived from boneless or ground veal. It is important to remember that some meat cutters may remove the shoulder meat with the shank (see Fig. 12.19A). This is a matter of store merchandising policy.

2. Stitch the shoulder meat toward the center of the roast (see Fig. 12.19B).

   Caution: Keep your fingers clear from the point of the needle.

   Note: When tieing a boneless veal shoulder using the tunnel method, it is advisable to place the shoulder meat into the cavity and stitch the meat into place.

3. Place the blade end of the shoulder toward the center of the roast and stitch into place. (See Fig. 12.19C.)

   Note: This method will square off the roast into a rectangular shape. Some meat cutters may omit this step. This is often the reason for the roast being cooked unevenly. It is important to remember that the circumference of the roast should be uniform in shape (even in thickness).

4. Place 1 or 2 more stitches along the length of the roast. (See Fig. 12.19C.)

   Note: This will aid you in shaping the roast.

5. Place the loose guide string along the top and bottom portion of the roast.

6. Tie evenly-spaced cross strings starting at the thickest portion of the roast (see Fig. 12.19D).

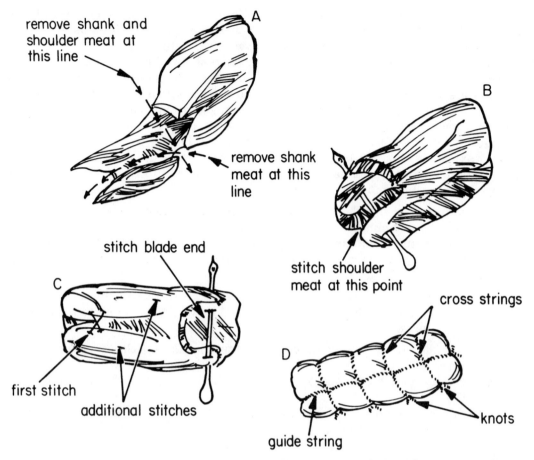

FIG. 12.19. STEPS TO TAKE TO TIE THE BONELESS LIFTED VEAL SHOULDER INTO A ROAST

VEAL SHOULDER PROCESSING AND MERCHANDISING TIPS

Some stores are equipped with tieing machines or "Jet-Net" machines. When tieing roast from the boneless shoulder, some meat cutters will stitch both ends of the shoulder before tieing the guide strings and cross strings with the tieing machine. It is important to remember to remove the shoulder and shank meat from the boneless shoulder before placing the shoulder in the funnel of the Jet-Net machine.

Roasting requires the dry heat method. If the shank and shoulder meat remain in the roast, the tendon area of the shoulder and shank meat will become tougher with cooking and therefore may discourage future sales.

There are variations which meat cutters should try in merchandising the veal shoulder. Offer the consumer some 3-in-1 combination or 4-in-1 com-bination of veal items from the veal shoulder. For example, the blade steaks may be removed with the bone in. Bone the remainder of the shoulder, remove the shank and shoulder meat and cut into cubes for stew. Tie the clod section for a roast. Place the three items together in one boat. Another example would be as follows: Bone the entire shoulder. Cut the shank and shoulder meat for stew. Tie the clod section for a roast. Cut cutlets from the blade section of the shoulder. Place all these items in one boat.

Meat cutters should use their own innovations to increase sales. There are many methods to employ in merchandising. Do not hesitate to change methods of merchandising as necessary. Variety is helpful to the consumer.

SEAMING AND SLICING THE BONELESS LIFTED SHOULDER

The methods used in seaming and slicing the individual muscles in the lifted shoulder will vary according to the meat cutters skill and knowledge. The average amount of muscles located in the shoulder are approximately 16–18. Each muscle, when seamed, will vary in size and tenderness depending upon the section of the shoulder from which the muscle was cut. Some meat cutters may use every muscle in the shoulder for slicing, while others will use only certain muscles in accordance with their skill or in accordance with store merchandising policies. Basically, there are four large muscles which should be used for slicing into thin cutlets. These muscles are similar to those present in the long beef shoulder except that they are smaller in size; they are the clod (cross-rib muscle), the triangle muscle (flat iron), the chuck tender muscle, and the thin muscle on the flat surface of the blade bone (mush steak muscle). These muscles will represent approximately 50% of the boneless shoulder, and are considered to be tender. Meat cutters may disagree upon which muscles are to be sliced as cutlets and which are to be merchandised other than cutlets. Methods of merchandising will vary from store to store according to the meat cutters skill and knowledge. Some chain stores and supermarkets rarely bone lifted veal shoulders to be merchandised into cutlets because of the processing time involved and the high cost of labor. These may not be the only causes in every case. It may also be due to the lack of skill and knowledge on the part of the meat cutter. The following are suggested methods for seaming, trimming, and slicing the boneless shoulder.

1. Remove the thin muscle (mush steak) at the natural seam located between the clod and the thin muscle. (See Fig. 12.20A.)
2. Remove the thin membrane from both sides of the thin muscle (Fig. 12.20B).
3. Butterfly the thin muscle by slicing the muscle in half lengthwise (see Fig. 12.20C).

   Caution: Keep the blade of the knife level with the surface of the cutting table. It is advisable to keep the item that is being sliced close to the edge of the table.

4. Separate the chuck tender muscle from the triangle muscle as shown in Fig. 12.21A.
5. Remove the thin membrane around the entire surface of the muscle (see Fig. 12.21B).
6. Remove the tendon in the center of the muscle by dividing the muscle in half lengthwise (see Fig. 12.21C).

   Note: Some meat cutters will omit this step and proceed to cut cutlets before removing the tendon in the center of the muscle. This is a matter of store merchandising practice.

7. Butterfly each half by slicing the muscle lengthwise. (See Fig. 12.21D.)

   Caution: Keep the blade of the knife level with the surface of the cutting table.

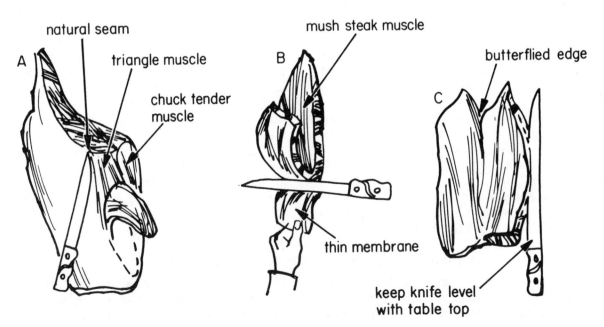

FIG. 12.20. TO MAKE CUTLETS FROM THE THIN MUSCLE TAKEN FROM THE FLAT SURFACE OF THE BLADE BONE, (A) REMOVE THE THIN MUSCLE AND (B) THE MEMBRANE, THEN (C) BUTTERFLY

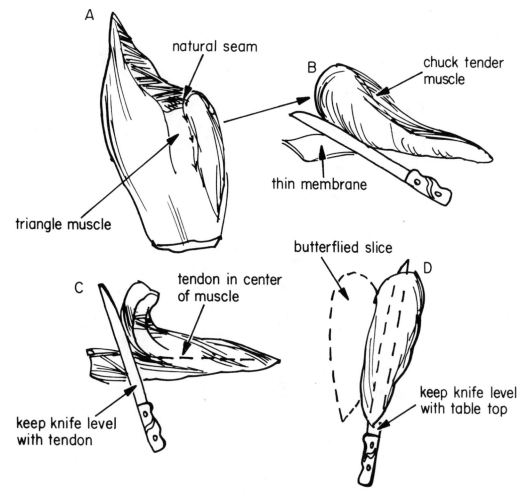

FIG. 12.21. TO SLICE CHUCK TENDER MUSCLE INTO CUTLETS: (A) REMOVE THE CHUCK TENDER MUSCLE; (B) THEN REMOVE THE THIN MEMBRANE FROM THE MUSCLE AND (C) THE TENDON IN THE CENTER OF THE MUSCLE; THEN (D) BUTTERFLY EACH HALF

Note: Some meat cutters prefer not to butterfly slices, especially if the chuck tender muscle is quite large in size. This will depend upon the type of veal merchandised.

8. Separate the triangle muscle from the clod muscle at the natural seam as shown in Fig. 12.22A.

9. Remove the thick tendon in the center of the muscle by splitting the muscle lengthwise (see Fig. 12.22B). Remove any thin membrane remaining on both sides of the muscle.

Note: Keep the knife level with the tendon to remove half of the muscle and then reverse the muscle and remove the tendon on the other half of the muscle.

10. Butterfly slices from each half that has been cut crosswise. (See Fig. 12.22C and 12.22D.)

Note: Some meat cutters may not cut the muscle crosswise before slicing the cutlets. They may prefer to slice the entire muscle lengthwise. This is a matter of the meat cutter's choice. Both methods are acceptable.

11. Separate the clod muscle (cross-rib) from the shoulder meat at the natural seam as shown in Fig. 12.23A.

12. Remove the thin membranes on both sides of the clod muscle.

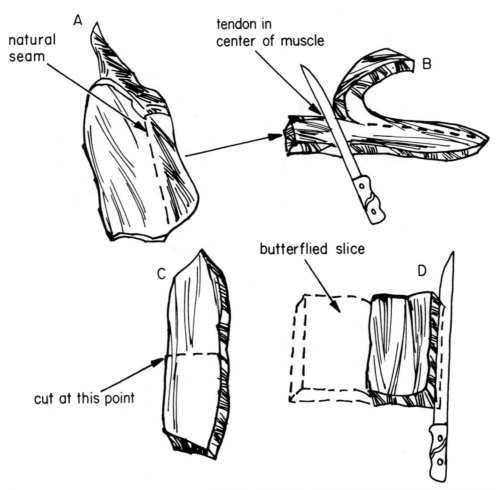

FIG. 12.22. TO SLICE TRIANGLE MUSCLE INTO CUTLETS: (A) REMOVE TRIANGLE MUSCLE AND (B) TENDON THROUGH CENTER OF THE MUSCLE; THEN (C) CUT EACH HALF OF MUSCLE CROSSWISE AND (D) BUTTERFLY EACH HALF

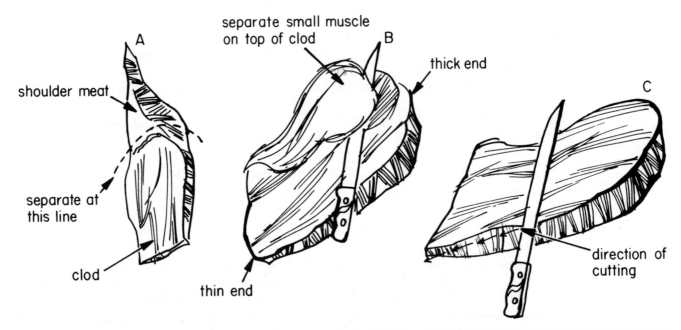

FIG. 12.23. TO SLICE CLOD MUSCLE INTO CUTLETS: (A) REMOVE AS SHOWN AND (B) THEN REMOVE THICK MEMBRANE IN CENTER OF CLOD MUSCLE BEFORE (C) SLICING MUSCLE THINLY ON AN ANGLE

Note: Some meat cutters may remove the thick membrane in the center of the clod by lifting off the small muscle on the top of the clod near the thick end. (See Fig. 12.23B.)

13. Slice the clod muscle on an angle as shown in Fig. 12.23C to produce a wider slice of cutlet.

Note: Butterfly the end piece.

The remainder of the shoulder can be merchandised as veal stew, cubed veal steaks, ground veal (such as a meat loaf item), veal patties, mock chicken legs, and other items. It is important to remember that the cutlets sliced from these four muscles should be mixed and placed in a No. 1 boat.

Try to keep the weight of the boat under 1 lb, because of the high retail selling price. It will also help the consumer with small families to choose items of smaller weights. It is not advisable to slice cutlets from the remainder of muscles in the shoulder because of the tough connective tissues within these muscles. Some meat cutters will mix 2 or 3 small slices and place these muscles through a steak tenderizing machine to cut all the tissues within the muscles. Place these slices (4 to 6), separated by patty paper, in a No. 2 boat and label the package "cubed veal steaks."

PROCESSING THE VEAL NECK

Wholesalers who break down veal foresaddles into subprimal cuts generally process a 3-rib neck. Methods will vary from wholesaler to wholesaler depending upon price and the merchandising practice of the wholesaler in different regions of the country. The neck represents approximately 18–19% of the veal foresaddle. The short veal rack is removed from the neck portion by cutting between the third and fourth rib bone; this results in a 3-rib neck. (Refer back to Fig. 10.2 in Unit 10 for primal and subprimal cuts of veal and the cutting of a veal loin and veal rack from the veal carcass.)

The bones contained in the veal neck (double) are the neck bones (7), the rib bones (6), the feather bones, and the chine bone. The veal neck is generally considered to be the least desirable of all the subprimal cuts from the veal foresaddle because of the tough muscle structure in the neck region of the carcass. Retailers should be knowledgeable with the methods of veal cookery to enable them to process the veal neck into various retail cuts. The neck contains a large percentage of bones. Merchandising these bones with other retail items may discourage the consumer from making future purchases of veal items derived from the neck. This will result in a loss of tonnage in sales. It is important to remember that veal necks should be boned before cutting into retail cuts. The exceptions are the first three rib bones in a veal neck. Methods of merchandising the veal neck will depend upon the skill and knowledge of the meat cutter. The following are some suggested methods for merchandising the veal neck.

PROCESSING SPECIAL FRENCH RIB CHOPS

1. Place the veal neck on the movable carriage of the band saw with the rib bone (cut surface) facing the back plate. See Fig. 12.24A.

   Caution: It is advisable to check the band saw blade to see that it is sharp. Change the blade if necessary. Dull blades tend to tear the meat and cause a pulling action rather than a cutting action.

2. Remove three slices from the veal neck by cutting between each rib bone.

   Caution: Keep your fingers clear from the path of the blade.

3. Cut down the center of the backbone from each double cut chop (see Fig. 12.24B).

4. Remove the chine bone, feather bone, and the back strap from each chop (Fig. 12.24C).

5. Remove approximately 1 in. of meat from the top portion of the rib bone (see Fig. 12.24D).

6. Score the top surface of the chop with an up and down motion with the steak knife. Repeat this operation on the other side of the chop (Fig. 12.24E).

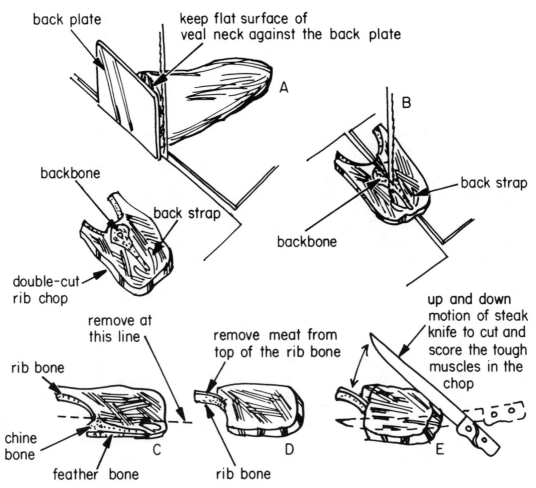

FIG. 12.24. FOLLOW STEPS A, B, C, D, AND E TO CUT SPECIAL FRENCH RIB CHOPS

7. Place approximately 1–2 oz of ground veal on the cut scored chop. Repeat step No. 6.

   Note: It is advisable to dip the knife in hot water to prevent the meat from adhering to the knife. Do not cut too deeply; merely blend the ground veal into the cut surface of the chop.

8. Place the chop on patty paper and place only 2 chops in a No. 2 boat for small chops and a No. 10 boat for large chops.

   Note: If no patty paper is available make your own squares from parchment paper.

BONING THE VEAL NECK

1. Cut down the center of the backbone and loosen the chine meat from the backbone. (See Fig. 12.25.)
2. Continue cutting toward the tips of the feather bones.
3. Cut around each feather bone (Fig. 12.25).
4. Reverse the position of the veal neck and repeat steps No. 2 and 3 and remove the backbone in one piece (see Fig. 12.25).

Merchandising the Boneless Neck

Remove the back strap and any discolored meat around the throat area. The neck can then be cut into cubes for a veal stew item or tied into a roast. (See Fig. 12.26.) A prepared mixture for stuffing can be placed in the center before tieing the roast.

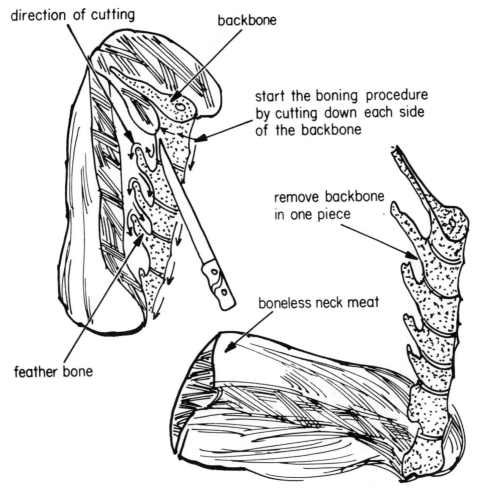

direction of cutting

backbone

start the boning procedure by cutting down each side of the backbone

remove backbone in one piece

boneless neck meat

feather bone

FIG. 12.25. IN BONING THE VEAL NECK, BACKBONE CAN BE REMOVED IN ONE PIECE AS SHOWN

Some meat cutters may slice the boneless neck into cutlets. This is not advisable because of the tough tissues in the neck region and the method of cooking cutlets may even toughen the cutlet more. An excellent retail item for the boneless neck is to cut it into small cubes and label the product, "Veal Cubes for Veal and Peppers."

PROCESSING THE SQUARE-CUT CHUCK

The veal square-cut chuck is similar to that of the square-cut chuck of lamb with the exception of its size. The veal square-cut chuck is much larger in size than that of the lamb. (Refer back to the text on primal and subprimal cuts of veal in Unit 10.) The veal square-cut chuck is processed from the veal foresaddle in various forms. The form will depend upon the packers' methods of processing. Some packers may cut between the third and fourth rib bone; this will produce a 3-rib chuck. Some packers may cut between the fourth and fifth rib bone to process a 4-rib chuck; and cutting between the fifth and sixth rib bone will process a 5-rib chuck. The region of the country and the method employed by the packer will determine the cutting procedure.

Wholesalers in the Northeastern part of the country rarely cut square-cut chucks of veal. This may be due to the larger size of the retail cut items, such as veal chops, derived from the chuck. Consumers may become confused and discouraged because some retailers may refer to these shoulder veal chops as veal steaks because of the large size. Some chains and supermarkets may cut chops from square-cut chucks that are smaller in size and of lesser weight. This may not always be feasible. Supply and demand are important factors regulating the price at the wholesale markets. Another important factor to remember is that veal carcasses of lighter weight generally have a higher content of natural moisture because of their immaturity. This may cause the muscle structure to be spongy and

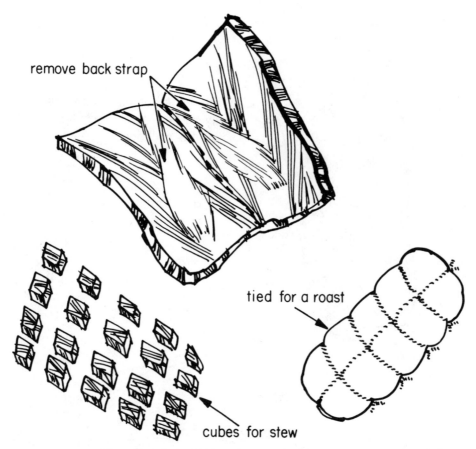

remove back strap

tied for a roast

cubes for stew

FIG. 12.26. THE BONELESS NECK CAN BE MERCHANDISED CUT INTO CUBES FOR STEW MEAT OR TIED FOR A ROAST

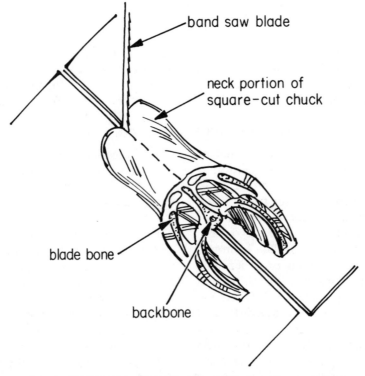

band saw blade

neck portion of square-cut chuck

blade bone

backbone

FIG. 12.27. SPLIT THE SQUARE-CUT CHUCK INTO TWO VEAL SHOULDERS

sloppy which, in turn, may cause difficulty for the meat cutter when cutting retail items from the square-cut chuck. Some meat cutters may overcome this problem by placing the veal in the freezer for a short period of time. This process is called chilling. This again may not be the answer. When the cut portion of the item is on display, the juices from the cell walls may be released rapidly and combine with water and blood, causing a shorter shelf-life (decrease in merchandising time).

Methods employed by retailers in cutting square-cut chucks from veal foresaddles will vary according to their merchandising needs and store practices.

Stores that merchandise the entire breast for a roast item may remove the breast and foreshank before cutting between the fifth and sixth rib bone to separate the rack from the chuck. Stores who do not merchandise the entire breast for a roast item, may first cut between the fifth and sixth rib bone, and then proceed to remove the brisket and foreshank from the chuck. Methods will vary with meat cutters when processing the square-cut chuck from the veal foresaddle. The following are some suggested methods for processing and merchandising the square-cut chuck.

CUTTING SHOULDER CHOPS FROM THE SQUARE-CUT CHUCK

1. Place the square-cut chuck on the table of the band saw with the neck portion facing the blade. (See Fig. 12.27.)
2. Split the chuck down the center of the backbone.

   Caution: Keep your fingers clear from the path of the blade.

   Note: The resulting two sides are now called veal shoulders.

3. Place the shoulder on the band saw with the bone side down and the round bone facing the back plate as in Fig. 12.28.

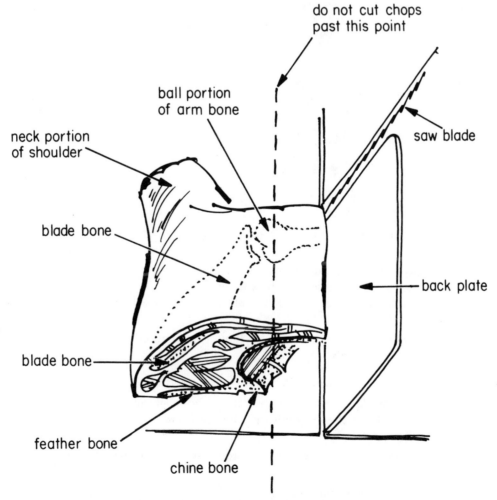

FIG. 12.28. WHERE TO CUT ROUND-BONE CHOPS FROM THE VEAL SHOULDER

4. Remove approximately 3 to 4 round-bone chops at the desired thickness.

   Caution: Do not pull the chop through the blade with your free hand. Guide the chop through the blade carefully.

5. Place the shoulder on the band saw with the blade bone facing the back plate as in Fig. 12.29.

6. Cut blade chops at the desired thickness (usually from 6 to 8 chops).

7. Package the chops after trimming into a No. 8, 9, or 12 size boat, placing 2 chops to a boat. If the chops are large, it is advisable to place one chop to a boat.

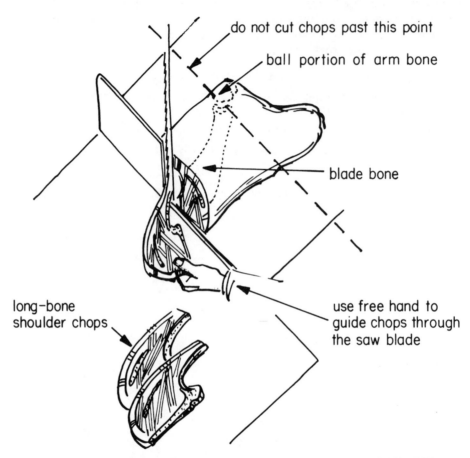

FIG. 12.29. WHERE TO CUT LONG-BONE CHOPS FROM THE VEAL SHOULDER

8. The remainder of the shoulder and the neck meat should be trimmed of excess fat and cut into cubes for stew. The stew meat can be merchandised by placing it with combination boats of chops and stew meat. This is a matter of store merchandising practice.

   Note: The neck portion can also be boned and cubed for stew or made into ground veal items.

BONING THE SQUARE-CUT SHOULDER

1. Place the veal shoulder on the bench with the bone side up. (See Fig. 12.30A.)

2. Cut the underside of the rib bones (5) loosening all the meat from the rib bones (Fig. 12.30A).

   Note: This method is known as scalping. It will produce a smoother boned surface.

3. Continue to cut toward the feather bones, loosening all the meat from the feather bones. (See Fig. 12.30B.)

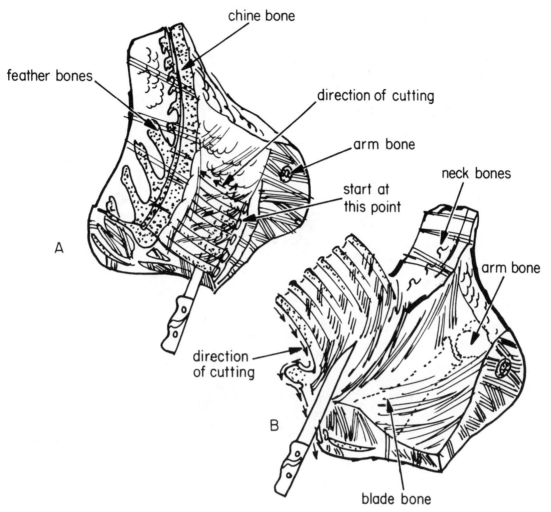

feather bones

chine bone

direction of cutting

arm bone

start at
this point

A

direction
of cutting

neck bones

arm bone

B

blade bone

FIG. 12.30. ENTIRE BACKBONE CAN BE REMOVED IN ONE PIECE

Caution: Keep your free hand away from the cutting action of the knife.

4. Continue to scalp out the neck bones to free the bones all in one piece. (See Fig. 12.30B.)

   Note: Do not discard these bones. Cut the bones into 2-in. pieces and merchandise them as veal neck bones.

5. Cut along the side of the arm bone up to and through the arm bone socket. Free all the meat from the arm bone. (See Fig. 12.31A.)

6. Cut along the side of the blade bone. Catch the seam at the socket portion of the blade bone. Lift the meat from the flat surface of the blade bone. (See Fig. 12.31A.)

7. Catch the seam by scraping at the exposed end of the ridge of the blade bone. (See Fig. 12.32A.)

8. Pull the blade bone free from the shoulder. Remove all cartilages remaining on the shoulder. (See Fig. 12.32B.)

Tieing the Boneless Square-Cut Chuck into a Roast

Meat cutters will vary their methods in tieing the boneless shoulder. Some may remove the clod section before tieing the shoulder, especially in large veal shoulders. These clods can be merchandised as veal cutlets, which will retail at a higher selling price. Some meat cutters may tie 2 shoulder clods together by reversing the ends of

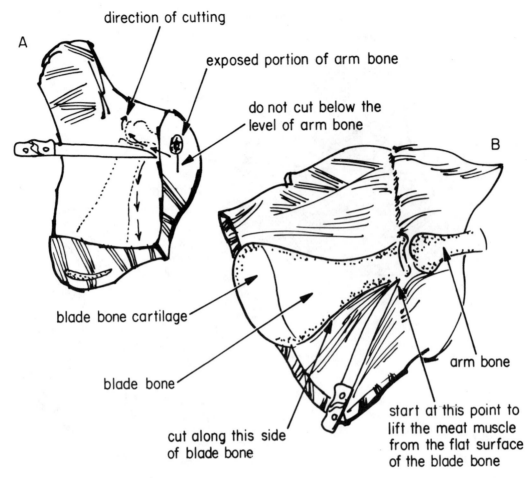

FIG. 12.31. TO BONE THE SQUARE-CUT SHOULDER, FIRST REMOVE THE ARM BONE AS SHOWN
IN A AND B

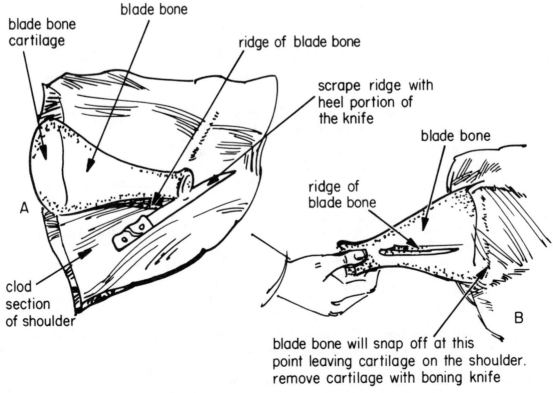

FIG. 12.32. THEN REMOVE THE BLADE BONE AS SHOWN IN A AND B

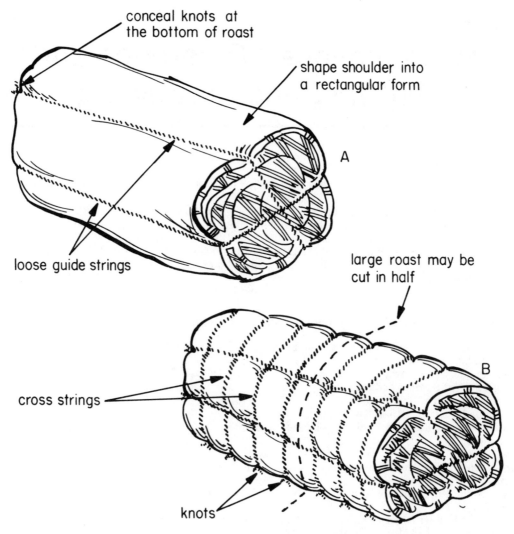

conceal knots at
the bottom of roast

shape shoulder into
a rectangular form

A

loose guide strings

large roast may be
cut in half

B

cross strings

knots

FIG. 12.33. BONELESS SHOULDER CAN THEN BE TIED INTO ONE OR TWO ROASTS USING (A)
LOOSE GUIDE STRINGS AROUND LENGTH AND (B) CROSS STRINGS AROUND CIRCUMFERENCE

2 roasts and string-tieing girthwise. The method used by retailers will vary from
store to store.

1. Place a double guide string lengthwise on the shoulder. Shape the roast into a
   rectangular shape (see Fig. 12.33A).
2. Place cross strings evenly at approximately 1 to 1½ in. apart. (See Fig. 12.33B.)

   Note: If roast is large, it is advisable to cut the roast in half.

Recommended Reference and Self-Instruction Reading

Textbooks

ASHBROOK, F. G. 1955. Butchering, Processing, and Preservation of Meat. Van Nostrand Reinhold, New York, N.Y. 10001.

LEVIE, A. 1970. The Meat Handbook, 3rd Edition. Avi Publishing Co., Westport, Conn. 06880.

McCOY, J. H. 1972. Livestock and Meat Marketing. Avi Publishing Co., Westport, Conn. 06880.

POTTER, N. N. 1973. Food Science, 2nd Edition. Avi Publishing Co., Westport, Conn. 06880.

REYNOLDS, P. H. 1963. The Complete Book of Meat. M. Barrows & Co., West Caldwell, N.J. 07006.

U.S. DEPT. OF AGRICULTURE. 1974. Meat and Poultry Inspection Regulations. U.S. Government Printing Office, Washington, D.C. 20250.

ZIEGLER, P. T. 1966. The Meat We Eat. Interstate Printers and Publishers, Danville, Ill. 61832.

Sources of Valuable Manuals, Bulletins, and Pamphlets

American Insurance Association, 85 John Street, New York, N.Y. 10038.
    Your Guide to Safety in Meat Packing
American Lamb Council, 520 Railway Exchange Bldg., 909 17th St., Denver, Colorado.
    Something Different Starring Today's Lamb
    Mt. Vernon Prime Rib of Ramb Roast
    Rolled Shoulder of Lamb, "Roast Royale"
American Meat Institute, 59 East Van Buren St., Chicago, Ill. 60605.
    Ideas with Meat
    New Meat Manual
    Pork Operations in The Meat Industry (authored by David Mackintosh, Dept. of Animal Husbandry, Kansas State University)
Chain Store Age, Lebhar-Friedman, Inc., 2 Park Ave., New York, N.Y. 10061.
    Meat Manual
Koch Supplies, Inc., 1411 West 29th St., Kansas City, Missouri 64108.
    Meat Curing Principles and Modern Practices
    Successful Meat Curing
National Association of Meat Purveyors, 120 S. Riverside Plaza, Chicago, Ill. 61616.
    Meat Buyers Guide to Portion Control Meat Cuts
    Meat Buyers Guide to Standardized Meat Cuts
National Live Stock and Meat Board, 36 S. Wabash Ave., Chicago, Ill. 60603.
    A Hog's Not All Chops
    Facts About Pork
    Guide for Cutting Lamb Chops (prepared for the U.S. Armed Forces)
    Handbook on Cutting Lamb (prepared for the U.S. Armed Forces)
    Lamb Cutting Manual
    Lessons on Meat
    Merchandising Heavy Lamb
    Merchandising Legs of Pork (Fresh Hams)
    Merchandising Pork Loins
    Merchandising Pork Shoulders
    Meat Evaluation Handbook
    Pork Loin Profits
    Uniform Retail Meat Identity Standards
    101 Meat Cuts
National Safety Council, 425 N. Michigan Ave., Chicago, Ill. 60611.
    Booklet prepared by Meat Packing, Tanning and Leather Products, Hand Knives
New York State Food Merchants Association, 280 N. Central Ave., Hartsdale, N.Y. 10530.
    Meat Label Identification List (approved by the N.Y. State Dept. of Agriculture and Markets, May 1972)
Rath Packing Co., Waterloo, Iowa.
    Sales Training Course
Super Market Institute, 200 East Ontario St., Chicago, Ill. 60611.
    Meat Merchandising

Meat and Produce Wrapping
Meat Department Sanitation
Meat Guide and Standards Manual
University of Missouri, Extension Division, Columbia, Missouri.
Handling Prepackaged Meat in Retail Stores, Manual *64*
U.S. Dept. of Agriculture, Marketing Service, Washington, D.C. 20402.
USDA Grades for Pork Carcasses, Bulletin *49*
USDA Yield Grades for Lamb
Official U.S. Standards for Grades of Lamb, Yearling, Mutton, and Mutton Carcasses, Bulletin *123*
All About Meat, Bulletin *3643*
Official U.S. Standards for Grades of Lamb, Yearling Mutton, and Mutton Carcasses; Slaughter Lambs, Yearlings, and Sheep, Part *53*, Subpart B-Standards
Institutional Meat Purchase Specifications for Fresh Pork, Series *400*
State of New York, Dept. of Agriculture and Markets, Building 8, State Campus, Albany, N.Y. 12226.
Meat for Sale at Retail, Part *260*

Index

NOTES

NOTES

NOTES

NOTES

NOTES

NOTES

NOTES

NOTES